SENIOR CHEMISTRY

NOTES

COLES EDITORIAL BOARD

Bound to stay open

Publisher's Note

Otabind (Ota-bind). This book has been bound using the patented Otabind process. You can open this book at any page, gently run your finger down the spine, and the pages will lie flat.

ABOUT COLES NOTES

COLES NOTES have been an indispensible aid to students on five continents since 1948.

COLES NOTES are available for a wide range of individual literary works. Clear, concise explanations and insights are provided along with interesting interpretations and evaluations.

Proper use of COLES NOTES will allow the student to pay greater attention to lectures and spend less time taking notes. This will result in a broader understanding of the work being studied and will free the student for increased participation in discussions.

COLES NOTES are an invaluable aid for review and exam preparation as well as an invitation to explore different interpretive paths.

COLES NOTES are written by experts in their fields. It should be noted that any literary judgement expressed herein is just that — the judgement of one school of thought. Interpretations that diverge from, or totally disagree with any criticism may be equally valid.

COLES NOTES are designed to supplement the text and are not intended as a substitute for reading the text itself. Use of the NOTES will serve not only to clarify the work being studied, but should enhance the reader's enjoyment of the topic.

ISBN 0-7740-3411-4

CONTENTS

UNIT 1

INTRODUCTION

Science is an attempt to accumulate and organize experimental information. Once regularities have been found an effort is made to explain them. For example, the early work in sciences such as Botany and Stellar Spectroscopy (study of star light) was concerned chiefly with classification; the work which is being done now in these fields is attempting to explain the observed regularities at the molecular and atomic level.

The interpretation of such experimental results involves inductive reasoning — the formation of a general rule from some particular observations. Inductive reasoning thus makes generalizations about a whole group after sampling some of the group. Some ideas discovered by inductive reasoning (e.g. the Law of Universal Gravitation) have been tested successfully many times, while others (e.g. all moving objects tend to become stationary) have been shown to be false.

A scientific "model" or theory is a set of concepts or ideas attempting to describe a particular phenomena. A "model star" is a set of equations relating to pressures and temperatures at various levels within a star. A "model" for a gas is the postulate that gases are composed of particles moving about and colliding elastically (the collisions conserve kinetic energy). The equations governing the motion of the gas particles are the same as those governing the motion of a billiard ball or any other visible particle, e.g. kinetic energy $= \frac{1}{2} mv^2$. The pressure exerted by a gas may then be likened to the pressure exerted by kernels of corn which are popping in a container.

Any experimentally measured number is of necessity approximate: only counting numbers, the integers, are exact. Any calculation based upon approximate numbers must yield an answer which is itself approximate. Just as a chain is as strong as its weakest link, a calculated number is no more accurate than the least accurate number which was used in the calculation. If the least accurate number in an operation of addition or subtraction has N decimal places, then the answer should be rounded off to N decimal places. If the least accurate factor in an operation of multiplication or division has N digits, then the answer should have N digits.

Example: What is the concentration of the solution formed when 10 gm of sodium chloride, NaCl, are dissolved in one litre of aqueous solution which was initially 2.3 molar NaCl?

Solution: 1 mole of NaCl = 23.0 + 35.5 = 58.5 gm.
     58.5 gm of NaCl = 1 mole of NaCl

$$1 \text{ gm of NaCl} = \frac{1}{58.5} \text{ mole of NaCl}$$

     10 gm of NaCl = 10/58.5 = 0.17 mole of NaCl
     (N = 2 digits)

The solution initially had 2.3 moles of NaCl in one litre. The solution now has 2.3 + 0.17 = 2.47 moles of NaCl in one litre. Because the least accurate term has one decimal place, the answer should be to one decimal place. Therefore the new concentration is 2.5 moles of NaCl in one litre or 2.5 molar (2.5 M).

The estimation of errors is generally a difficult procedure; if the errors were known they would no longer be errors but would be included in the calculations as "correction factors". For example, in accurate work involving thermometers the observed temperature reading and the true value differ slightly because part of the mercury column is in the air of the room rather than in the substance which is having its temperature measured. A "stem correction" formula is used to calculate the magnitude of the correction.

Experimental results can often be best shown graphically. Figure 1-1 shows the relation between mass of carbon tetrachloride liquid and the volume of the sample.

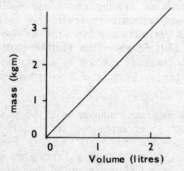

Fig. 1-1. The relation between mass and volume for carbon tetrachloride. The slope yields the density of the liquid, 1.6 kgm per litre.

Molecules and Atoms

Avogadro's Hypothesis states that equal volumes of gases at the same temperature and pressure contain equal numbers of molecules.

It has been found experimentally that one gram molecular weight (one mole) of oxygen gas weighs 32 gm and occupies a volume of 22.4 litres at S.T.P., standard temperature (0°C) and standard pressure (one atmosphere).

Because of these facts one can accurately find molecular weights of gases. If a sample of a gas is found to weigh twice as much as an equal volume of oxygen at the same temperature and pressure, then by Avogadro's Principle the gram molecular weight of this gas is $(2 \times 32$ gm) or 64 gm.

Example: Find the G.M.W. of carbon dioxide given that the density at S.T.P. is 1.964 gm per litre.

Solution: 22.4 l. of O_2 at S.T.P. weigh 32.0 gm.

$$\therefore \text{ The density of } O_2 \text{ at S.T.P.} = \frac{32.0 \text{ gm}}{22.4 \text{ l}} = 1.428 \frac{\text{gm}}{\text{litre}}$$

$$\therefore CO_2 \text{ is } \frac{1.964 \text{ gm/l}}{1.428 \text{ gm/l}} \text{ or } 1.375 \text{ times more dense than } O_2.$$

By Avogadro's Hypothesis, one litre of oxygen contains the same number of molecules as one litre of carbon dioxide at the same temperature and pressure. The individual molecules of carbon dioxide must be 1.375 times heavier than the oxygen molecules, and the gram molecular weight of carbon dioxide must be 1.375×32.0 gm. = 44.0 gm.

One of the counting units in Chemistry is Avogadro's number, 6.02×10^{23} particles per mole (or 6.02×10^{23} molecules per gram molecular weight). It has been found experimentally that in the gaseous state 6.02×10^{23} particles at S.T.P. occupy 22.4 litres.

Molecules are made up of particles called atoms; it is believed that each molecule of oxygen contains two atoms of oxygen. This concept is based on experimental evidence which shows that one mole of oxygen can react with two moles of carbon monoxide to yield two moles of carbon monoxide. Because 6.02×10^{23} molecules of oxygen can be used to generate 12.04×10^{23} molecules of carbon dioxide, it appears that each oxygen molecule can split into two identical atoms. Therefore, one half of an oxygen molecule or one oxygen atom unites with one carbon monoxide molecule yielding one carbon dioxide molecule.

UNIT 2

ENERGY EFFECTS IN CHEMICAL REACTIONS

Heat and Chemical Reactions —

By its very nature, any chemical reaction involves transfer of energy. In some cases energy is released (e.g. burning carbon); in other cases energy is absorbed (e.g. heating potassium chlorate). If energy is absorbed, then the products have more energy than the reactants and this energy may later be recovered.

For example, carbon burns in air to release 94,000 calories or 94 kilocalories (94 kcal) for each mole of carbon consumed.

$$C + O_2 \longrightarrow CO_2 + 94 \text{ kcal}$$

If the carbon is oxidized using water vapour the following reaction occurs absorbing 31.4 kcal/mole of carbon,

$$C + H_2O + 31.4 \text{ kcal} \longrightarrow CO + H_2$$

When the equimolar mixture of products called water gas is oxidized, the following changes occur:

$$CO + \tfrac{1}{2}O_2 \longrightarrow CO_2 + 67.6 \text{ kcal}$$
$$H_2 + \tfrac{1}{2}O_2 \longrightarrow H_2O(g) + 57.8 \text{ kcal}$$

Note that the total energy released is 67.6 + 57.8 = 125.4 kcal/mole of carbon originally consumed in the production of the water gas.

Heat Content of a Substance, H — measures the amount of energy stored in a mole of the substance during its formation. For example, the formation of 1 mole of carbon dioxide from the elements is accompanied by a release of 94 kcal of energy. Therefore the heat content, H, of carbon dioxide is — 94 kcal/mole. The negative sign indicates that heat is removed from the system, or that carbon dioxide has less energy than the reactants.

Heat Effect of a Reaction, ΔH — is the difference between the heat contents of the products and the heat contents of the reactants.

$$H_{\text{Products}} - H_{\text{Reactants}} = \Delta H$$

This quantity, ΔH, may be found even if neither H_{products} or $H_{\text{reactants}}$ is known. The situation is similar to that in which an observer wishes to find the difference in elevation above sea level of the top and bottom of a vertical flag pole. In the latter case, he need only measure the length of the pole; in the former he need measure only the energy transferred during the reaction.

If the products have more energy than the reactants, then heat is absorbed, and ΔH is positive:

$$C + H_2O \longrightarrow CO + H_2 \qquad \Delta H = 31.4 \text{ kcal}$$

If the products have less energy than the reactants, then heat is released and ΔH is negative.

$$C + O_2 \longrightarrow CO_2 \qquad \Delta H = -94 \text{ kcal}$$

Note that the value of ΔH for the latter reaction yields the heat content of carbon dioxide.

Finding the Total Heat Effect in a Sequence of Reactions — If a sequence of chemical reactions occurs, then the overall heat of reaction is the sum of the individual heats of reaction. The heat generated by the reaction of a mole of a substance is a constant characteristic of that reaction. Its value does not depend on subsequent reactions. The procedure then is as easy as finding the change in "cash on hand" after making a series of sales and purchases. Recall the water gas reaction and the subsequent burning:

$$C + H_2O \longrightarrow CO + H_2 \qquad \Delta H = 31.4 \text{ kcal}$$
$$CO + \tfrac{1}{2}O_2 \longrightarrow CO_2 \qquad \Delta H = -67.6 \text{ kcal}$$
$$H_2 + \tfrac{1}{2}O_2 \longrightarrow H_2O(g) \qquad \Delta H = -57.8 \text{ kcal}$$

Summing:

$$C + H_2O + CO + \tfrac{1}{2}O_2 + H_2 + \tfrac{1}{2}O_2 \longrightarrow CO + H_2 + CO_2 + H_2O$$
$$\Delta H = -94 \text{ kcal}$$

The numbers of moles of water, hydrogen and carbon monoxide on each side of the overall equation are equal. The equation becomes, in its simplest form,

$$C + O_2 \longrightarrow CO_2 \qquad \Delta H = -94 \text{ kcal}$$

This is in agreement with previous knowledge: in effect one mole of carbon has been oxidized with the release of 94 kcal.

Measuring Reaction Heat Experimentally: Known quantities of reactants are introduced into a reaction chamber; the reaction may then be triggered by passing an electric current through a high resistance wire in contact with the reactants. The reaction vessel is generally surrounded by water which is able to absorb relatively large amounts of heat with small temperature changes. The water jacket is thermally insulated from the surroundings and a temperature measuring device,

such as a thermometer or a thermocouple, is placed in the water.
The quantity of heat energy which is released may then be calculated.

Calculating Heats of Reaction — Standard tables are available which
show the heats of reaction of many elements at 25°C and 1 atmosphere. For example:

(A) $\frac{1}{2}N_2 + \frac{1}{2}O_2 \longrightarrow NO$ $\Delta H = 21.6$ kcal

(B) $\frac{1}{2}N_2 + O_2 \longrightarrow NO_2$ $\Delta H = 8.1$ kcal

This information may then be used to make calculations about the
reactions of compounds.

Example: Calculate the heat of reaction for the following:

$$NO + \frac{1}{2}O_2 \longrightarrow NO_2$$

Solution: Consider that the nitric oxide, NO, is being broken down
into its constituent elements and that simultaneously the nitrogen
dioxide, NO_2, is being generated out of its constituent elements.
The decomposition of NO may be shown by either the negative or
the reverse of equation (A), the sythesis of NO_2 is shown by equation (B)

(-A) $-\frac{1}{2}N_2 - \frac{1}{2}O_2 \longrightarrow -NO$ $\Delta H = -21.6$ kcal

or

(-A) $NO \longrightarrow \frac{1}{2}N_2 + \frac{1}{2}O_2$ $\Delta H = -21.6$ kcal

(B) $\frac{1}{2}N_2 + O_2 \longrightarrow NO_2$ $\Delta H = 8.1$ kcal

Sum (-A) + (B): $NO + \frac{1}{2}O_2 \longrightarrow NO_2$ $\Delta H = -13.5$ kcal

Heats of reaction for many processes involving molecular reactants
and products may thus be calculated from the information contained
in a list of heats of reaction of elements.

Example: Given the heats of reaction for the following reactions:

$H_2 + S + 2O_2 \longrightarrow H_2SO_4$ $\Delta H = -194$ kcal

$S + O_2 \longrightarrow SO_2$ $\Delta H = -71$ kcal

$H_2 + \frac{1}{2}O_2 \longrightarrow H_2O(g)$ $\Delta H = -57.8$ kcal

calculate the energy required to synthesize sulphur dioxide from
sulphuric acid.

$$H_2SO_4 \longrightarrow SO_2 + H_2O + \frac{1}{2}O_2$$

Solution: Consider that the H_2SO_4 is being broken down into its constituent elements and that the products are being generated from their constituent elements,

$$H_2SO_4 \longrightarrow H_2 + S + 2O_2 \qquad \Delta H = \quad 194 \text{ kcal}$$

$$S + O_2 \longrightarrow SO_2 \qquad \Delta H = -71.0 \text{ kcal}$$

$$H_2 + \tfrac{1}{2}O_2 \longrightarrow H_2O(g) \qquad \Delta H = -57.8 \text{ kcal}$$

Summing: $H_2SO_4 + S + O_2 + H_2 + \tfrac{1}{2} O_2 \longrightarrow H_2 + S + 2O_2 + SO_2 + H_2O$

Cancelling quantities common to each side gives:

$$H_2SO_4 \longrightarrow SO_2 \quad + H_2O + \tfrac{1}{2}O_2$$

The overall $\Delta H = 194 + (-71.0) + (-57.8) = 65.2$ kcal.

The final answer is 65 kcal. The digit 2 which appears in the first decimal place in the calculated answer is not significant because we do not know the digit in the first decimal place of the quantity 194 kcal. Generally, an unknown quantity when subtracted from or added to a known quantity produces an unknown quantity.

Conservation of Energy —

Energy is the ability to do work or the ability to exert a force through a distance. Energy is neither created nor destroyed in ordinary changes: it may be transformed.

Kinetic energy is possessed by all moving objects. The amount of work which the object can do increases as either the mass or velocity of the object increases. Potential energy is found in objects which have had work done on them as they were "raised" in opposition to a force. For example, a brick raised in the air has the work done on it stored in it as gravitational potential energy; a negative pith ball removed from a positively charged sphere has the work done stored in the pith ball as electrical potential energy; a nail withdrawn from a magnet has magnetic potential energy.

In each of these three cases the object when released, will "fall" toward the attracting object and the potential energy will be convented to kinetic energy.

In chemical reactions energy is also conserved. If 18 gm of liquid water, (1 mole), is electrolyzed, then 68.3 kcal of electrical energy are consumed and the gaseous products have 68.3 kcal more energy than the reactants:

$$H_2O \ (liquid) \longrightarrow H_2 + \tfrac{1}{2}O_2 \qquad \Delta H = 68.3 \text{ kcal}$$

If the generated hydrogen and oxygen are burned to form water vapour at 25°C and one atmosphere, then 57.8 kcal would be released:

$$H_2 + \tfrac{1}{2}O_2 \longrightarrow H_2O(g) \qquad \Delta H = -57.8 \text{ kcal}$$

Condensation of the vapour to liquid at 25°C would release an additional 582 cal/gm or 10.5 kcal/mole. The total energy released by the combustion and the subsequent condensation to form one mole of liquid water at 25°C is $57.8 + 10.5 = 68.3$ kcal. This is the same quantity of energy which was used to electrolyze the mole of water at 25°C.

The Energy Stored in a Molecule —

All molecules have kinetic energy of vibration. Gaseous molecules also have kinetic energy of translation and rotation. Chemical energy is found stored in the shared electron pairs of bonds which hold the atoms together. The molecules have electrical potential energy relative to each other, the amount depending upon the degree of separation. Each electron has electrical potential energy with respect to all neighbouring nuclei.

The sum of these individual energies is the molecular heat content. The molar heat content is then 6.02×10^{23} times greater than the average molecular heat content.

When heat energy is supplied to a solid element the kinetic energy of vibration increases until melting occurs. The continued addition of heat eventually causes boiling and, if very high temperatures are reached, nuclear changes. When heat energy is supplied to a solid compound, the same general sequence of physical changes occurs. Before sufficient energy has been put into the system to cause nuclear changes, the chemical bonds will be broken. For example, solid cane sugar decomposes at 186°C and has no liquid phase, potassium chlorate melts at 368°C but the liquid decomposes at 400°C with no definite boiling point. Gaseous N_2O_4 decomposes when heated to form NO_2.

Energy Stored in a Nucleus —

This energy is not released in chemical changes because nuclei are not altered during a chemical reaction.

A few atomic nuclei are unstable and spontaneously disintegrate, while some others which are stable or relatively stable may be bombarded with atomic projectiles to produce a high energy reaction in which the mass of the nucleus changes. When the reaction is over the total number of nucleons (protons and neutrons) and the total electrical charge is found to be unaltered.

For example, all atoms of uranium (Atomic Number = 92) have 92 protons: some atoms of uranium have 143 neutrons. These atoms have 235 nucleons or a mass number of 235. When a sample of U-235 atoms is bombarded with neutrons, nuclear changes result. One possible reaction is:

$$\ce{^{235}_{92}U} + \ce{^{1}_{0}n} \longrightarrow \ce{^{141}_{56}Ba} + \ce{^{92}_{36}Kr} + 3\,\ce{^{1}_{0}n} + \text{energy}$$

where $\ce{^{1}_{0}n}$ represents a neutron of mass $= 1$ and charge $= 0$

Note that the number of positive charges before and after is constant (92) and that the total number of nucleons is constant (236).

Experiment: To measure the amount of heat released (heat of reaction) between solid sodium hydroxide and hydrochloric acid.
This may be done in two ways.

(a) Add equimolar quantities of hydrochloric acid and solid NaOH and measure the heat released.

or

(b) Dissolve the NaOH in water and measure the heat released during dissolution. Then mix the base solution with an equal number of moles of acid and measure the heat released.

To measure the heat released in either case the following equation is used.

heat gained = mass × temperature change × specific heat

Remember that the container also gains heat and that this term must be taken into consideration when calculating the overall heat release. If the solutions are dilute, then it may be assumed that the mass of one cc. of solution is one gram and that the specific heat is that of water (1 calorie per gram per centigrade degree).

total heat gained = (mass × temperature change) *liquid*
+ (mass × temperature change × specific heat) *container*

UNIT 3

THE RATES OF CHEMICAL REACTIONS:

Rate measurements involve the determination of the amount of change which occurs in a period of time. For example, the rate of sedimentation of silt in a lake or the rate of growth of a tree can be measured in "inches per year". In chemical reactions the rate measurement is a statement of how quickly the reactant is vanishing or of how quickly the product is being generated.

$$\text{Rate of reaction} = \frac{\text{quantity of substance consumed or produced}}{\text{time interval}}$$

For example: if the reaction has aqueous $KMnO_4$ (purple solution) as a reactant, the change in concentration (in moles/litre) can be easily measured as the colour fades. Hence the rate of change, in $\frac{\text{moles / litre}}{\text{sec}}$, may be found.

In some cases it is easier to measure the amount of product, e.g.

$$Ca\,CO_3 + 2\,HCl \longrightarrow CaCl_2 + H_2O + CO_2$$

The progress of the reaction is determined by measuring the volume of the generated gas and the rate is expressed as moles of CO_2 per second or moles of CO_2 per minute.

FACTORS AFFECTING RATES OF REACTION:

Nature of Reactants — Reactions between simple ions are rapid while those between molecular compounds or those involving the breakdown of compound ions are generally slow. The implication is that reactions which do not involve bond breaking or formation are usually rapid at room temperature; those reactions in which bonds are rearranged tend to be slow at room temperature.

Concentration — if a reaction is to occur then the reactants must have an opportunity to come in contact with or collide with each other. If the reaction involves fluids (gases or liquids) then the number of collisions per second and the rate may be increased by increasing the concentration. This may be done by procedures such as adding more solute, removing some solvent, or increasing the pressure of any gases involved.

If the reaction is between a solid (e.g. magnesium) and a fluid (oxygen or hydrochloric acid), then the number of collisions per second is largely determined by the extent of the surface area of the solid.

Reaction Mechanism – A chemical reaction which seems to be complex (i.e. which seems to require many molecules colliding at the same place at the same instant of time) is likely proceeding by a sequence of simple reactions, each involving the collision of two particles. The oxidation of 4 molecules of gaseous HBr at 500°C requires only 1 molecule of oxygen:

$$4HBr + O_2 \longrightarrow 2H_2O + 2\ Br_2$$

This reaction is actually the apparent or overall result of three simpler reactions:

$$HBr + O_2 \longrightarrow H\text{-}O\text{-}O\text{-}Br \quad \text{slow}$$
$$H\text{-}O\text{-}O\text{-}Br + HBr \longrightarrow 2\ HOBr \quad \text{fast}$$
$$2\ HOBr + 2\ HBr \longrightarrow 2H_2O + 2Br_2 \quad \text{fast}$$

The product of the first reaction, H-O-O-Br, has an unstable peroxide bond -O-O- and is almost automatically consumed as quickly as it is generated. Similarly the HOBr (hydrogen hypobromite) is readily consumed. The rate controlling process is the first reaction and anything which increases the rate of this reaction must automatically increase the rate of the overall reaction.

Quantitative Effect of Concentration – The rate of reaction must depend upon the number of collisions which occur between the reacting particles. Doubling the concentration of either reactant doubles the number of collisions.

If the reactants are gases, then the concentration of each gas may be expressed in moles per litre or in terms of the pressure which that gas exerts (partial pressure). In the above example of the oxidation of HBr: rate (overall) is proportional to (pressure exerted by HBr) and (pressure exerted by O_2) or

$$\text{rate} = \text{constant} \times (p_{HBr}) \times (p_{O_2})$$

(Recall that the area of a triangle is proportional to both the base and height: the constant is ½). In the case of a particular chemical reaction the value of the rate constant k depends on the temperature.

In the general case, when one mole of reactant A reacts with one mole of reactant B to generate products, the rate at which the reaction progresses is

$$k \times (\text{concentration of A}) \times (\text{concentration of B})$$

As the reaction proceeds and the concentration values decline at equal rates, the rate of the reaction falls markedly and continuously.

Effect of Temperature on Reaction Rates: – We live in a gaseous sea of oxygen and nitrogen: the nitrogen atoms can form several oxides but they do not react with the oxygen of the air. The reason is this: the collisions do not have sufficient energy to cause bond rearrangements, in the same way that two slowly colliding eggs do not have enough energy to break their shells. If the reaction is to occur, then the collision must involve a minimum amount of energy, the "threshold energy" for that particular reaction.

In a pure sample of gas molecules at a certain temperature one will find a range of molecular velocities and hence kinetic energies. The range of kinetic energies may be measured experimentally by allowing a sample of the gas to diffuse down a tube to a target. As in a race, the fastest particles (highest kinetic energy) reach the target first. The lowest kinetic energy particles strike the target last. If the target is moving we obtain a distribution of particles, ranging from those which were travelling quickly and arrived first to those which were travelling slowly and arrived last.

For comparison, think of someone standing at the base of an upward bound escalator and dropping a mixture of sand, clay and chalk-dust over the escalator. Because of air resistance the finest particles will hit the escalator last and hence start the trip upward later than the particles which moved quickly. A distribution of the particles, based on speed of fall, will be obtained.

In the case of streaming gas molecules a distributed pattern of molecules is sublimed onto a relatively cold moving target. The majority of the molecules will hit the central portion of the target; molecules with energy higher than average will be sublimed onto the leading part of the target. Molecules with low kinetic energy and speed will hit the trailing part of the target. The "target" itself may be a rotating disk or a moving strip.

The results of such an experiment are shown in Figure 3-1.

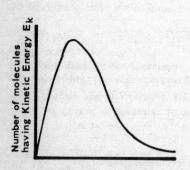

Fig. 3-1. The distribution of energy in a typical gas sample. Relatively few molecules have either very high or very low kinetic energies.

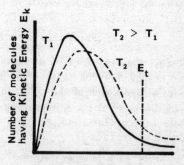

Fig. 3-2. The effect of temperature on the energy distribution in a gas. At the higher temperature more molecules have the threshold energy E_t.

An increase in temperature causes a general shift to higher energy conditions and to an increase in the number of molecules having energy greater than the threshold value, as is shown in Figure 3-2.

If the reaction is slow, then few molecules have the threshold energy. An increase in temperature will increase the number of molecules which possess this minimum amount of energy required for the reaction.

THE ROLE OF ENERGY IN RATES OF REACTION

When a rubber ball bounces, the kinetic energy decreases to zero as the ball stops for an instant, then the ball regains kinetic energy as it starts moving in the direction opposite to the original. The kinetic energy was temporarily transformed to potential energy in the deformed and compressed rubber of the ball. As the molecules spring back to their original position they cause the ball to be accelerated.

A similar type of energy storage occurs when molecules collide and react. As the reactant molecules approach they slow down, loose KE and form an unstable structure with higher potential energy than the separated molecules. (If the molecules are moving too slowly this structure will not be formed, just as a slowly moving rubber ball is not deformed much on impact.) This intermediate structure, called an activated complex, is unstable and will soon decompose to form either the original reactants (no reaction) or products (new bonds formed, old ones broken). The threshold energy to successfully form the activated complex from the reactants is called the activation energy.

A potential energy diagram for a reaction shows "total Potential Energy of System" on the vertical axis and the "Reaction co-ordinate" on the horizontal axis, (Figure 3-3).

The reaction co-ordinate indicates the progress of the reaction. The left side of the reaction co-ordinate represents the separated reactant molecules. The extreme right side represents the separated product molecules. The intermediate regions represent the successive configurations which are encountered as the reactant molecules approach and rearrange to form the activated complex.

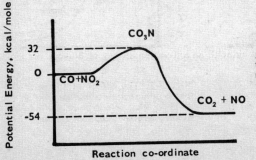

The potential energy diagram for the reaction between $CO + NO_2$, CO_3N represents the unstable activated complex.

18

The graph shows that if the activated complex flies apart to form the products CO_2 and NO, then the final PE of the system is less than the initial. The kinetic energy of the system has been increased and the more quickly moving molecules will be "hotter": heat energy has been released.

Heat of Reaction and Activation Energy — An exothermic reaction is one in which the reactants are at a higher potential energy than the products (Figure 3-4).

$$CO + NO_2 \longrightarrow \text{activated complex} \longrightarrow CO_2 + NO$$

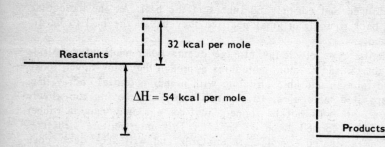

Fig. 3-4 An exothermic reaction reaction with an activation energy of 32 kcal per mole of CO oxidized.

An endothermic reaction is one in which the products are at a higher potential energy than the reactants (Figure 3-5).

$$CO_2 + NO \longrightarrow \text{activated complex} \longrightarrow CO + NO_2$$

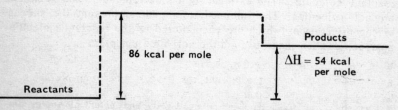
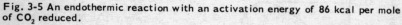

Fig. 3-5 An endothermic reaction with an activation energy of 86 kcal per mole of CO_2 reduced.

In these examples, experiments show that the activated complex has 32 kcal more energy than $(CO + NO_2)$ and 86 kcal more energy than $(CO_2 + NO)$. Thus, the potential energy of $(CO + NO_2)$ is 54 kcal greater than the potential energy of $(CO_2 + NO)$.

In general, the heat of reaction ΔH is the difference in potential energies of the reactants and the products. Accordingly ΔH may be calculated by finding the difference in activation energies of the forward and the reverse reactions.

Catalysts — are substances which increase the rate of a reaction without being used up or permanently changed.

Many catalysts do this by reacting with the reactants to form a new activated complex with a lower activation energy than that of the complex produced in the uncatalyzed reaction. When this new complex (containing the catalyst) decomposes, it forms products (or reactants) and regenerates the catalyst. The catalyst is then available to repeat the procedure. Because the complex in the catalyzed reaction has a lower potential energy than the complex in the uncatalyzed reaction, it is formed more readily.

The catalyzed complex is formed readily and may decompose to form either reactants or products. Accordingly, the rate of the reverse reaction will be increased and its activation energy will be lowered.

Examples of catalysis are found in the reaction of potassium permanganate $(KMnO_4)$ with oxalic acid $(H_2C_2O_4)$ and in the decomposition of formic acid (H_2CO_2) in the presence of a strong acid.

In the first instance, the slow reaction of $KMnO_4$ supplies Mn^{+2} ions which act as catalysts, forming a new activated complex with lower potential energy. Thus the reaction tends to speed up.

In the second case, the hydrogen ions supplied by the strong acid add to the hydroxyl (OH) group in the formic acid molecule

$$H-C{\overset{\displaystyle O}{\underset{\displaystyle OH}{}}} \quad + \quad H^+ \longrightarrow H-C{\overset{\displaystyle O}{\underset{\displaystyle OH_2^+}{}}}$$

The proton addition to the hydroxyl oxygen atom causes an electron shift from the carbon atom toward this oxygen atom. The weakened bond between the carbon atom and the oxygen atom then breaks.

$$HCOOH_2^+ \longrightarrow HCO^+ + H_2O$$

The unstable HCO^+ decomposes to release a molecule of carbon monoxide (CO) and a hydrogen ion.

Some catalysts (such as platinum which is used in hydrogenation) are solids which hold or absorb reactants on their surfaces, with an accompanying weakening of bonds.

EXPERIMENTS:

(1) The reaction between iodate ion, IO_3^-, and hydrogen sulphite ion, HSO_3^-, in the presence of starch and water.

The reaction which is being timed in this experiment is

$$IO_3^- + 3HSO_3^- \longrightarrow I^- + 3SO_4^{-2} + 3H^+$$

When the HSO_3^- ion is completely consumed, neutral molecular iodine, I_2, can be formed in a secondary reaction between the iodide ion, I^-, and IO_3^-.

$$5I^- + 6H^+ + IO_3^- \longrightarrow 3I_2 + 3H_2O$$

If starch is present in the solution, then a reaction between molecular iodine and starch produces a distinctive blue colour. The appearance of this colour coincides with the complete consumption of HSO_3^- ions.

If the initial concentration of HSO_3^- ions in a set of solutions is kept constant, then it is found that the time for reaction decreases (rate increases) as the concentration of IO_3^- is increased.

If the concentration of both HSO_3^- ion and IO_3^- ion is kept constant, then it is found that as the temperature rises the rate of reaction increases (or that the time for the reaction of HSO_3^- decreases).

(2) The reaction of potassium permanganate, $KMnO_4$, with oxalic acid, $H_2C_2O_4$, and sulphuric acid in water.

In this case the time required for completion of the reaction is found by noting the time required for the purple colour of MnO_4^- ion to vanish.

$$2KMnO_4 + 5H_2C_2O_4 + 3H_2SO_4 \longrightarrow K_2SO_4 + 2MnSO_4 + 8H_2O + 10CO_2\uparrow$$

If the initial concentration of $KMnO_4$ is kept constant, then it is found that increasing the concentration of either acid increases the rate of the reaction. The effect of a temperature increase is an increase in the rate of reaction. The addition of a small quantity of a salt containing Mn^{+2} ion to the reactants shortens the reaction time, indicating that this ion is a catalyst in this reaction.

Potassium permanganate solutions also react with solutions which contain iron (II) ions. The reaction is:

$$5\,Fe^{+2} + MnO_4^- + 8H^+ \longrightarrow 5Fe^{+3} + Mn^{+2} + 4H_2O$$

UNIT 4

EQUILIBRIUM IN CHEMICAL REACTIONS.

In many reactions the products react to regenerate the original reactants (reversible reactions). In a typical system of this type we first observe that the concentration of the reactants decreases and the concentration of the products increases. But as the product concentration increases, the rate of regeneration of the reactants will increase. When the rate of regeneration of the reactants has risen so that it is equal the rate of c o n s u m p t i o n of the reactants, then changes in the system will no longer be visible and the system will be in a "state of equilibrium."

The recognition of the existence of a state of equilibrium in a system is based upon the constancy of the physical properties of the system. The following three examples illustrate this.

(1) When solid iodine is placed in an alcohol-water solution the molecules of iodine break away from the crystal and dissolve. As the concentration of iodine in the solution rises, more iodine molecules per second are going to hit the solid iodine and precipitate or crystallize. At some stage the dissolved iodine concentration will rise to a level such that the rate of crystallization will equal the rate of dissolution. The brown colour and the density of the solution will then be constant but there will be, at the microscopic level, a constant exchange of individual molecules between the solid and the solution. The existence of this exchange may be shown by placing some radioactive iodine solid in contact with the saturated solution. The saturated solution is soon found to contain radioactive atoms of iodine.

(2) Another equilibrium situation is encountered when a liquid evaporates into a closed evacuated container. As more molecules move from the liquid state to the vapour state, the number of vapour molecules per second which chance to move into the liquid increases. As the liquid continues to evaporate at a constant rate (at constant temperature) the rate of condensation increases until it equals the rate of evaporation. The existence of a state of equilibrium in this case is indicated by the constant concentration of gas molecules above the liquid. This concentration is most easily measured by finding the pressure exerted by the vapour above the liquid.

(3) An example of chemical equilibrium is found in the system involving the gases nitrogen dioxide NO_2 and nitrogen tetroxide N_2O_4.

$$N_2O_4 \text{ (colourless)} \longrightarrow 2NO_2 \text{ (brown)}$$

$$2NO_2 \longrightarrow N_2O_4$$

The larger molecule N_2O_4 becomes less stable as the temperature rises.

If a sample of N_2O_4 and NO_2 at room temperature is heated to 100°C, then the rate of decomposition of N_2O_4 increases with a resulting decrease in the concentration of this species. The increased concentration of NO_2 results in more collisions which could produce N_2O_4; this tends to maintain the N_2O_4 concentration. Eventually, when a state of equilibrium is established at 100°C, the rate of decomposition of the diminished N_2O_4 population will equal the rate of recombination of the increased NO_2 population. A constant intensity brown colour will be obtained which will be darker than that which was observed at room temperature.

Similarly, cooling a sample of N_2O_4 and NO_2 from room temperature to 0°C favours the recombination of NO_2 molecules. The concentration of N_2O_4 increases. This increase in the concentration of N_2O_4 tends to increase the rate of decomposition of these molecules (even if N_2O_4 is more stable at lower temperatures). Simultaneously, the declining concentration of NO_2 tends to decrease the rate of recombination. Eventually the two rates will become equal and the brown colour will become constant.

The above equations may be combined as follows:

$$N_2O_4 \rightleftharpoons 2 NO_2$$

The double arrow is read "in a state of equilibrium with". The equation thus indicates that:

(a) a molecule of N_2O_4 may decompose to form 2 molecules of NO_2,

(b) 2 molecules of NO_2 may combine to form 1 molecule of N_2O_4.

(c) The two reaction rates are equal.

The relative quantities of products and reactants at equilibrium depend upon the temperature, pressure (or concentration if in solution) and in general the nature of the molecules involved. In some cases the reverse reaction proceeds at a very low rate and the equilibrium strongly favours the products. In such cases the existence of an equilibrium state may be overlooked because the initial reaction may appear to have gone to completion.

Altering the state of equilibrium means changing the relative amount (or percent) of the reactant which has been consumed. This is accomplished by varying the factors mentioned above — temperature and concentration (or pressure for gaseous reactions). Two examples illustrate this.

Concentration effects on the state of equilibrium are seen in the reactions which occur between solutions containing thiocyanate ions, SCN^-, and iron (III) ions, Fe^{+3}. The complex ion which is formed has a characteristic brown colour.

$$Fe^{+3} + SCN^- \rightleftharpoons FeSCN^{+2}$$

If a crystal of $FeCl_3$ is added to this system in equilibrium, then the brown colour deepens. This indicates the production of more $FeSCN^{+2}$ and a decrease in SCN^- ion concentration. Similarly the addition of a crystal of potassium thiocyanate, KSCN, to the system in equilibrium results in the darkening of the solution with an accompanying decrease in the concentration of Fe^{+3} ions.

Thus by increasing the concentration of reactant A the rate of the forward reaction is increased and the concentration of reactant B is decreased. Eventually a new state of equilibrium will be reached, as the forward reaction tends to slow down and the reverse reaction tends to speed up.

Temperature effects on the state of equilibrium have already been considered in the system:

$$N_2O_4 \rightleftharpoons 2\,NO_2$$

Generally, an increase in temperature will favour the endothermic reaction. A new state of equilibrium will be set up at the new temperature.

It should be noted that catalysts do not alter the state of equilibrium: they lower the activation energy, allowing a greater chance of forming the activated complex. The activated complex however may decompose to produce either reactants or products. Both reaction rates are increased by the same factor and the state of equilibrium characteristic of that temperature and concentration is reached sooner than it would be in the absence of the catalyst.

Attainment of Equilibrium

In some cases, such as the reaction of hydrogen and oxygen, the reaction is highly favoured by energy considerations, yet the reaction occurs so slowly that equilibrium is not established at room temperature.

$$H_2 + \tfrac{1}{2}O_2 \longrightarrow H_2O(g) \qquad \Delta H = -57.8 \text{ kcal/mole}$$

Le Chateliers' Principle — is a useful statement which summarizes the above information about equilibrium systems: "if an equilibrium system is subjected to a change, then processes occur that minimize or tend to partially counteract the imposed change."

Concentration and Le Chatelier's Principle:

$$Fe^{+3} + SCN^- \rightleftharpoons FeSCN^{+2}$$

If crystals of $FeCl_3$ are added to the solution when a state of equilibrium has been established, then the dissolving tends to increase the concentration of Fe^{+3} ions in the solution. This increase in concentration causes the formation of more $FeSCN^{+2}$ ions, i.e. a withdrawal of some Fe^{+3} ions from the solution.

The system in equilibrium has a built in tendency to maintain its existing state, a type of chemical inertia. (Recall from mechanics that moving objects tend to keep moving in straight lines; stationary objects tend to remain stationary). In the equilibrium system, if some concentration change is made which favours one of the reactions, then this reaction will speed up, consuming more of the reactants and thus tending to lower the rate.

Pressure and Le Chatelier's Principle:

In chemical equilibrium, pressure has very little effect on either reaction unless one or more of the substances is a gas. Changing the pressure on gaseous systems changes the concentration of the gases. An increase in pressure causes an increase in the number of moles/litre of all species. Consider the effect of a pressure increase on the following: $H_2O(g) \rightleftharpoons H_2 + \frac{1}{2}O_2$

The rate of the reverse reaction depends upon the concentrations of two species, each of which has been increased. Because the rate depends upon the concentration of both H_2 and O_2, the doubling of both concentrations would tend to quadruple the rate. Thus the reverse reaction is more favoured by increased pressure than is the forward reaction.

An increase in the pressure on any gaseous system tends to shrink the system into a smaller volume, causing the system to exert more pressure on the container. And, in equilibrium systems, the compression also favours the reaction in which the product has fewer moles than the reactant. The net effect of an increase in pressure is to cause a reduction in the number of moles present; this tends to reduce the pressure exerted by the system. An alternative way of stating this is: an increase in pressure tends to concentrate all species; the reaction with the smaller number of moles on the product side is always favoured by an increase in pressure.

Temperature and Le Chatelier's Principle:

When heat energy is added to a system the usual result is an increase in temperature. In equilibrium systems however the change in temperature may be slight or nil as in the case of an ice-water system. In the typical equilibrium system the endothermic reaction, which absorbs heat, will be favoured by the application of heat. This absorption of heat tends to minimize the temperature change. In the case of melting, the temperature change may be zero if sufficient solid is present.

Example: $N_2O_4 \rightleftharpoons 2\,NO_2$ $\Delta H = +\,14.1 \text{ kcal}$

or $\quad N_2O_4 + 14.1 \text{ kcal} \rightleftharpoons 2NO_2$

The addition of heat drives the forward reaction until a new state of equilibrium is established. The consumption of N_2O_4 results in increased concentration of NO_2. This tends to increase the rate of the reverse or back reaction. When the two rates become equal the equilibrium is re-established.

Application of Equilibrium Principles: — the Haber Process

Ammonia is a gas at room temperature and atmospheric pressure. It is used in the manufacture of fertilizers and explosives.

$$N_2 + 3H_2 \rightleftharpoons 2NH_3 \qquad \Delta H = -22 \text{ kcal}$$

The negative value of ΔH indicates that the forward reaction is exothermic: the product has less energy than the reactants.

If heat is added to this system in equilibrium, then the decomposition reaction, which absorbs heat, will be favoured.

Because the decomposition reaction is both endothermic and undesirable, a low temperature should be maintained.

If the pressure is increased, then the reaction producing the smaller number of moles will be favoured. In this case the forward reaction produces only 2 moles of product for each 4 moles of reactants consumed, and this "shrinking" reaction will be favoured by increased pressure.

In the industrial manufacture of ammonia, temperatures of about $500^\circ C$ are low enough to give a satisfactory state of equilibrium and are high enough to give a reasonable rate of reaction. A catalyst and moderate pressures of 350 atm. are used.

Quantitative Aspects of Equilibrium:

A full understanding of an equilibrium system requires the confirmation of generalizations by experimental measurements. In the case of chemical equilibrium an interesting pattern appears when measurements are made of concentrations of reactants in equilibrium systems.

Example: $Fe^{+3} + SCN^- \rightleftharpoons Fe\,SCN^{+2}$

At any constant temperature, it is found experimentally that the ratio of ionic concentrations

$$\frac{[Fe\,SCN^{+2}]}{[Fe^{+3}]\,[SCN^-]}$$

has a definite, constant value. The magnitude changes only with temperature. The square brackets indicate "concentration in moles per litre."

If Fe^{+3} ions are added, then the value of [SCN⁻] drops while that of [Fe SCN⁺²] rises. When equilibrium is restored the fraction has regained its initial value, which is characteristic of these substances at that temperature.

A slightly different case is encountered in the gaseous equilibrium system:

$$2 \text{ HI} \rightleftharpoons H_2 + I_2 \quad \text{or} \quad HI + HI \rightleftharpoons H_2 + I_2$$

Experiments indicate that the ratio which is constant is:

$$\frac{[H_2] \, [I_2]}{[HI] \, [HI]} \quad \text{or} \quad \frac{[H_2] \, [I_2]}{[HI]^2}$$

The "2" appears as a power of [HI] because 2 moles of HI appear in the equation.

In general, for a reaction such as

$$aA + bB \rightleftharpoons dD + eE$$

in which "a" moles of A react with "b" moles of B to form "d" moles of D and "e" moles of E, the ratio which is constant (at a given temperature) is, by experiment,

$$\frac{[D]^d \, [E]^e}{[A]^a \, [B]^b}$$

This value is called the equilibrium constant, K, for the system at that temperature.

It does not matter what change is made in, say, the concentration of D: the concentrations of A, B and E will automatically adjust to restore the constant value of the ratio.

The concentration of each substance must be raised to a power equal to the number of moles of that substance indicated in the equation. This experimental observation gives a clue about the origin of the expression for the equilibrium constant.

The rate of the forward reaction is $k_f \, [A]^a \, [B]^b$ where k_f is the rate constant for the forward reaction. If the equation shows that "a" moles of A are used, then the concentration of A must appear "a" times in the calculation of the rate. The rate of the back reaction is $k_b \, [D]^d \, [E]^e$ where k_b is the rate constant for the back reaction. At equilibrium, these two rates are equal:

$$k_f \, [A]^a \, [B]^b = k_b \, [D]^d \, [E]^e$$

or

$$\frac{k_f}{k_b} = \frac{[D]^d \, [E]^e}{[A]^a \, [B]^b} = K$$

Because k_f and k_b depend only on the temperature and the nature of the reactants, the ratio is a constant at a constant temperature.

In some cases the expression for the equilibrium constant becomes simpler than that shown above:

(a) If any of the substances are non-dissolving solids, then their concentration in the solution is zero and the concentration in the solid itself is constant. In such a case the expression for the equilibrium constant is written to show only variables.

Example: $Cu + 2\ Ag^+ \rightleftharpoons Cu^{+2} + 2\ Ag$

The equilibrium constant $= K = \dfrac{[Cu^{+2}]}{[Ag^+]^2}$

The unchanging values of the concentration of the uncombined metals, [Cu] and [Ag] are included in the overall constant.

(b) If the solvent is consumed (or generated) in the reaction, then the change in solvent concentration is usually negligible when the solution is dilute. For example, one litre (1000 ml) of dilute aqueous solution of a salt has approximately 1000 gm or $\dfrac{1000\ gm}{18\ \dfrac{gm}{mole}} = 55.5$ moles of water. The production (or consumption) of say, 1.8 gm water (0.1 mole) would change the water concentration by less than 0.2 per cent.

Example: The equilibrium constant for the ionization of water is 1×10^{-14}

$$H_2O \rightleftharpoons H^+ + OH^-$$

Calculate: (a) the concentration of hydrogen ions in distilled water.

(b) the relative number of water molecules ionized in distilled water.

Solution: $K = \dfrac{[H^+]\ [OH^-]}{[H_2O]}$

Because relatively few water molecules are ionized (water is a poor conductor) the value of $[H_2O]$ is taken as 55.5 moles/litre and has been included in K.

$$K = [H^+]\ [OH^-] = 1 \times 10^{-14}$$

28

Also, the equation indicates that $[H^+] = [OH^-]$ because each ioniz-
ing water molecule generates 1 hydrogen ion and 1 hydroxide ion.

$\therefore 10^{-14} = [H^+] [H^+]$ or $[H^+] = 10^{-7}$ moles/litre.

(b) 1 litre of water contains 55.5 moles of water and 10^{-7} moles of
hydrogen ions; i.e. of 555 moles of water, 10^{-6} moles are ionized, or, in 555 million moles of water, 1 mole is ionized, or,
of 555 million molecules of water, only 1 molecule is ionized.

Significance of the Value of the Equilibrium Constant — Because
the numerator of the expression for the constant involves factors for
product concentrations (raised to the appropriate power) and the denominator involves factors for the reactant concentration (raised to
the appropriate power) it follows that:

(a) If K is much greater than 1, then the numerator is much greater
than the denominator and the product concentrations will greatly
exceed the reactant concentrations.

(b) If K is much less than 1, then the reactant concentration at
equilibrium will be much greater than the product concentration.

(c) If K is approximately 1, then there will be comparable concentrations of reactants and products at equilibrium.

Factors which Determine Equilibrium — Opposing chemical reactions
proceed of their own accord toward the equilibrium state at rates
which depend only upon the individual rate constants and the declining concentration of the reactants and the rising concentration of the
products. The relative quantities of reactants and products at equilibrium, as shown by the equilibrium constant, are influenced by a
tendency to favour the state of lowest energy and a tendency to favour the state of greater randomness. An example of this may be seen
in the changes which occur as water is slowly heated through the
successive states of matter: solid — liquid — gas. At lower temperatures the solid is preferred, characterized by low energy and great
orderliness or low randomness. At the higher temperatures, the vapour
state with high energy and high randomness is favoured. Generally,
lower energy substances are favoured at lower temperatures, higher
randomness substances are favoured at higher temperatures.

UNIT 5

SOLUBILITY EQUILIBRIA

Situations involving the equilibrium between dissolved solute and undissolved solute are generally simple because:

(a) the undissolved solute is a solid whose constant concentration may be included in the equilibrium constant.

(b) there is frequently no chemical reaction. Example: when dark grey crystals of iodine are added to ethyl alcohol (colourless liquid) a brown solution is formed. When a state of equilibrium is attained, the rate of dissolving and the rate of crystallization are equal.

$$I_2 \text{ (solid)} \rightleftharpoons I_2 \text{ (dissolved)}$$

The equilibrium constant = K = I_2 (dissolved), the concentration of the saturated solution.

The Dynamic Nature of Solubility Equilibrium — Although there is no change in appearance of a system containing solid iodine in equilibrium with a saturated alcohol solution of iodine, millions of individual molecules are crystallizing every second and millions are dissolving every second. The equality of these two rates gives the illusion of cessation of change.

The rate of dissolving of any substance depends on the area exposed to the solvent. This is true for solid iodine dissolving in alcohol or for liquid water dissolving in air.

$$\text{Rate} = A \, k_d \text{ molecules/sec}$$

where A = surface area in sq. cm.

k_d = the rate constant for dissolving, the number of molecules leaving one sq. cm. in one second.

The rate of crystallization depends upon the surface area exposed, the rate constant for the crystallization, k_c (which is characteristic of the substance at the given temperature) and the concentration of the dissolved solute.

$$\text{Rate of crystallization} = A \times [\text{solute}] \times k_c$$

In the example of iodine in equilibrium with the saturated solution $k_d A = k_c A [I_2]$.

The equilibrium constant K is the ratio of the individual rate constants:

$$K = \frac{k_d}{k_c} = \frac{A \, [I_2]}{A} = [I_2]$$

Factors that Determine the Solubility of a Solid — Randomness is increased as the particles move from the orderly array of the solid to the dispersed state in solution. This effect tends to cause solids to dissolve.

Energy is usually absorbed when the particles are separated from the attractive forces which hold the solid array together. Thus the heat content rises and by energy considerations the undissolved solute is favoured.

Example: — in alcohol $$I_2 + 1.4 \text{ kcal} \rightleftharpoons I_2 \text{ (d)}$$

in carbon tetrachloride $$I_2 + 5.8 \text{ kcal} \rightleftharpoons I_2 \text{ (d)}$$

where I_2 (d) represents dissolved iodine.

In both instances the energy factor opposes the dissolving process. The opposition is stronger when carbon tetrachloride is the solvent. This is in accord with the experimental observation that the solubility of iodine is greater in alcohol than in carbon tetrachloride.

Temperature increases favour the endothermic process (usually dissolving) and the process producing greater randomness (always dissolving).

Solubility of a Gas in a Liquid — The dissolving of a gas in a liquid is generally similar to the condensation of a gas to a liquid: the molecules become more confined or less random and the molecules loose energy.

Randomness tends to oppose the dissolving process because the gas becomes more confined in the liquid.

Energy is released as the gas molecules dissolve and move into a state of lower energy. The tendency to move into a state of lower energy favours dissolving. If the randomness effects are the same for two typical gases, then the gas which releases more heat per mole on dissolving is more soluble.

Temperature increases favour the endothermic process (release of the gas) and the process producing the greater degree of randomness (generation of the gas).

Aqueous Solutions — Most chemical reactions which occur in solution have water as the solvent. The solutes may be generally classified as electrolytes or non-electrolytes.

Electrolytes are those substances which form electrically conducting solutions when dissolved in water. Some electrolytes are molecular substances, such as hydrogen chloride gas, whose molecules split and form ions when they react with water:

$$HCl \rightleftharpoons H^+ + Cl^-$$

Other electrolytes exist as ionic solids: the water is an agent which permits the separation of the previously existing positive and negative ions from the crystal lattice at a low temperature:

$$Na^+Cl^- \rightleftharpoons Na^+ + Cl^-$$

Generally, acids are typical of molecular substances which ionize in water; salts, particularly those of active metals and active non-metals, are ionic substances which·dissociate in water.

Any positive ions which are found in a solution may be attracted to a cathode and are called cations. Similarly, negative ions may be attracted to an anode and are called anions.

It has been found by experiment that certain types of ions tend to form soluble substances, while other types of ions tend to form insoluble substances. (A substance is considered soluble if it will form a solution of concentration 0.1 moles per litre or 0.1 M at room temperature).

Rule 1. The cations which form soluble substances are ammonium NH_4^+, H^+, and those of the alkali metals.

Rule 2. The anions which form soluble substances are nitrate, NO_3^- and acetate, CH_3COO.

For example, substances like potassium nitrate, KNO_3, and ammonium acetate, NH_4CH_3COO, are known to be soluble by either rule. Substances like potassium carbonate, K_2CO_3, and silver nitrate, $AgNO_3$, are known to be soluble by one of the rules.

Rule 3. Compounds containing the ions of the halogens (chloride Cl^-, bromide Br, iodide I^-) are soluble except for those containing the ions of certain unreactive metals known since antiquity: Cu^+, Ag^+, Hg_2^{+2} and Pb^{+2}. (Note that ions of mercury (I) occur in pairs).

Rule 4. Compounds containing sulphate ion, SO_4^{-2}, are generally soluble, except for those containing Pb^{+2} ions or ions of the high atomic weight alkaline earths Ca^{+2}, Sr^{+2}, Ba^{+2}, Ra^{+2}.

Rule 5. Compounds containing sulphide ion, S^{-2}, are insoluble, except for those whose cations are those of alkali metals (Group I) or of alkaline earths (Group II).

Rule 6. Compounds containing hydroxide ion OH^-, are insoluble, except for those whose cations are those of alkali metals (Group I) or the heavy alkaline earths Sr^{+2}, Ba^{+2}.

Rule 7. Compounds containing phosphate ion, PO_4^{-3}, sulphite ion, SO_3^{-2}, and carbonate, CO_3^{-2}, are insoluble, except for those whose cations are those of the alkali metals.

For example, the following substances are soluble:
$CaCl_2$, $MgBr_2$, AlI_3, $Al_2(SO_4)_3$, Na_2SO_4, CaS and $Ba(OH)_2$.

The following substances are insoluble:
AgCl, Hg_2Br_2, $CaSO_4$, ZnS, PbS, $Al(OH)_3$, $CaCO_3$ and $AlPO_4$.

The Equilibrium Law applied to Solubility — When a solid electrolyte is in a state of equilibrium with the saturated solution the concentration of the solid is a constant and accordingly is incorporated into the equilibrium constant. For example:

$$CaCl_2 \rightleftharpoons Ca^{+2} + 2Cl^-$$

$$\text{and } K = [Ca^{+2}] \, [Cl^-]^2$$

The equilibrium constant is called the "solubility product" and is represented by the symbol K_{sp}.

Example: Calculate the solubility product for copper (I) chloride, given that the concentration of the saturated solution is 5.7×10^{-4} moles per litre. This is one of the few slightly soluble chlorides.

Solution:
$$CuCl \rightleftharpoons Cu^+ + Cl^-$$

$$K_{sp} = [Cu^+] \, [Cl^-]$$

The dissolution of 5.7×10^{-4} moles of CuCl must release 5.7×10^{-4} moles of Cu+ ions and 5.7×10^{-4} moles of Cl^- ions to the solution.

i.e. $[Cu^+] = [Cl^-] = 5.7 \times 10.^{-4}$ moles per litre.

$$\therefore K_{sp} = (5.7 \times 10^{-4}) \times (5.7 \times 10^{-4})$$

$$= 32 \times 10^{-8} = (3.2 \times 10) \times 10^{-8}$$

$$= 3.2 \times 10^{-7}.$$

Conversely, the solubility of CuCl could be calculated if the solubility product were known. Knowing that $K_{sp} = 3.2 \times 10^{-7}$ it follows that:

$$[Cu^+] \, [Cl^-] = [Cu^+] \, [Cu^+] = [Cu^+]^2 = 3.2 \times 10.^{-7}$$

$$\therefore [Cu^+] = 5.7 \times 10^{-4}$$

and the quantity of CuCl which has dissolved must therefore be 5.7×10^{-4} moles per litre.

Predictions of Formations of Precipitates in Chemical Reactions — When solutions containing different ionic species are mixed, an insoluble product or precipitate will result if the product of the individual ionic concentrations, raised to the appropriate power, is greater than K_{sp} for the substance. It should be recalled that the

volume of the final solution will be the sum of the volumes of the individual portions which were mixed and that the concentrations will change accordingly. (If equal volumes are mixed, then the concentration of all ionic species is automatically halved even before any precipitation occurs).

Example: The solubility product of silver bromate, $AgBrO_3$, is 5.4×10^{-5}. Will a precipitate form if equal volumes of $0.03M$ silver nitrate, $AgNO_3$ and $0.01M$ sodium bromate, $NaBrO_3^-$ are mixed? ?

Solution: Four types of ions are present; the only two which are incompatible are Ag^+ and BrO_3^- .

$$\text{Immediately after mixing, } [Ag^+] = 0.015M$$
$$[BrO_3^-] = 0.005M$$

The product of the ionic concentrations =

$$[Ag^+] \ [BrO_3^-] = (1.5 \times 10^{-2}) \ (5 \times 10^{-3})$$
$$= 7.5 \times 10^{-5}$$

Because this product is greater (by about 40%) than K_{sp}, silver bromate, $AgBrO_3$, will precipitate from solution until the ion product $[Ag^+] \ [BrO_3^-]$ has been reduced to 5.4×10^{-5}. A state of equilibrium will then be established with the rate of dissolving equal to the rate of precipitation.

Precipitations, predicted from solubility rules and solubility — product constants, may be used to separate various ions or substances which are existing together in a solution. For example, Ag^+ ions could be removed from a solution containing $AgNO_3$ and $Cu(NO_3)_2$ by the addition of hydrogen chloride. The white solid silver chloride, $AgCl$, would be precipitated.

A substance may often be partially precipitated from a saturated solution by the addition to the solution of a substance of the same family. For example, if sodium bromate, $NaBrO_3$, is added to a saturated solution of silver bromate, $AgBrO_3$, the increase in $[BrO_3^-]$ drives the value of the ion product $[Ag^+] \ [BrO_3^-]$ above the K_{sp} value 5.4×10^{-5}. Silver bromate precipitates from the solution until the product $[Ag^+] \ [BrO_3^-]$ drops to 5.4×10^{-5}. Because sodium bromate is quite soluble, the $[BrO_3^-]$ value can be high when equilibrium is established. Accordingly the $[Ag^+]$ value can be very low and the precipitation of $AgBrO_3$ can be almost complete.

EXPERIMENT: The solubility — product constant of silver acetate. When silver acetate, $AgCH_3COO$, is placed in water it dissolves slightly:

$$AgCH_3COO \rightleftharpoons Ag^+ + CH_3COO^-$$

When equilibrium is established, $[Ag^+] = [CH_3COO^-]$

Any experiment which measures the equilibrium concentration of $[Ag^+]$ or the equilibrium concentration of $[CH_3COO^-]$ or the weight of $Ag CH_3COO$ which has dissolved per litre will do. For example, a known weight of AgCH₃COO could be added to a known volume of water, a saturated solution formed and the undissolved solute recovered and weighed. The number of moles of AgCH₃COO dissolved per litre may then be calculated. Squaring this value yields K_{Sp} for AgCH₃COO.

$$K_{Sp} = [Ag^+] \ [CH_3COO^-]$$

Another approach involves measuring the value of $[Ag^+]$. In this instance, a known volume of a saturated solution of AgCH₃COO is obtained. A clean, weighed piece of copper wire is added to the solution and allowed to stand for several hours. The reaction is:

$$Cu + 2Ag^+ \longrightarrow Cu^{+2} + 2Ag.$$

The copper wire is removed from the solution and cleaned, dried and weighed. The number of moles of copper which reacted is found by dividing the weight loss of the copper by the gram atomic weight of copper. The number of Ag^+ ions which reacted is twice this value. For example, a weight loss by the copper of 0.10 gm represents the reaction of 0.10/63.5 or 1.6×10^{-3} moles of copper and 3.2×10^{-3} moles of silver ions. Because the original volume of the solution which contained this much silver is known, the concentration in moles per litre is readily found. This value when squared yields K_{Sp}. Note that any error in weighing the copper becomes magnified as the measured number is first doubled and then squared. For example, if the true value is 10 and the measured value is 9, the error is 1 or 10%. Doubling the measured value yields a value of 18 while the true one is 20. The error is 2 or still just 10%. Squaring the measured value 9 yields 81, while squaring the true value 10 yields 100. The error is now 19%.

UNIT 6

AQUEOUS ACIDS AND BASES

Electrolytes are substances which form electrically conducting solutions when dissolved in water. If the substance exists chiefly as ions when dissolved, then it is a strong electrolyte. A weak electrolyte is substance which is only slightly ionized and the solute is chiefly in the molecular form.

Water is by this concept a weak electrolyte.

$$H_2O \rightleftharpoons H^+ + OH^-$$

The value for $K = \dfrac{k_f}{k_b} = [H^+][OH^-] = 1 \times 10^{-14}$. This indicates

that k for the recombination is 10^{14} greater than k for the ionization. Although the value of $[H^+]$ for pure water is only 10^{-7} moles per litre, this represents $10^{-7} \times 6.02 \times 10^{23} = 6.02 \times 10^{16}$ ions of hydrogen per litre. That is, 1 litre of water has 20 million hydrogen ions (and 20 million hydroxide ions) for each person on earth.

Concentration of H^+ and OH^- ions in Water

If the liquid is pure water, then $[H^+]$ must equal $[OH^-]$ because neither ion can be formed in pure water without the other. If an acid is added to water, then the acid releases many hydrogen ions. The ion product $[H^+][OH^-]$ is still the characteristic 1×10^{-14}. By Le Chatelier's Principle, the great increase in $[H^+]$ when the acid is added is partially offset by the reaction of more OH^- ions to form more water. The decrease in value of $[OH^-]$ balances the increase of $[H^+]$ and their product becomes 10^{-14} at equilibrium.

Similarly, if 0.4 gm (10^{-2} moles) of NaOH are added to 1 litre of water, the concentration of hydroxide ion will be 10^{-2} moles per litre, assuming complete ionization. The value of $[H^+]$ is low:

$$[H^+][OH^-] = 1 \times 10^{-14}$$

$$[H^+] \times 10^{-2} = 1 \times 10^{-14}$$

$$[H^+] = \frac{1 \times 10^{-14}}{10^{-2}} = \frac{10^{-12} \times 10^{-2}}{10^{-2}} = 10^{-12}$$

A change in $[OH^-]$ by a factor of 10^5 (from 10^{-7} to 10^{-2}) has been accompanied by a change in $[H^+]$ from 10^{-7} to 10^{-12}. As before, the influx of one species has been countered by an increased consumption of the other. The hydroxide ions are 10^{10} more common than the hydrogen ions in 0.01 M NaOH.

Many reactions which occur in aqueous solutions involve either H^+ or OH^- as catalysts or reactants or products in equilibrium systems. The final result may be varied tremendously by altering the relative concentrations of these ions.

Acids and Bases

An acid is a substance which can release hydrogen ions; examples: sulphuric acid H_2SO_4, nitric acid HNO_3, phosphoric acid H_3PO_4, chloric acid $HClO_3$, hydrochloric acid HCl, hydrosulphuric acid H_2S.

Acids are recognized by their conductivity (characteristic of all electrolytes) and their ability to liberate hydrogen gas when exposed to a metal such as magnesium.

$$2\,H^+ \ + \ Mg \longrightarrow Mg^{+2} \ + \ H_2 \uparrow$$

Acids react with certain large molecules (indicators) to form new substances with a characteristic colour: litmus becomes pink, bromothymol becomes yellow.

A base is a substance which can supply hydroxide ions OH^-, or which can remove hydrogen ions from an aqueous solution. Examples of the first kind include sodium hydroxide $NaOH$ and calcium hydroxide $Ca(OH)_2$; examples of the second kind include ammonia NH_3 and sodium carbonate Na_2CO_3.

Ammonia reacts with H^+ ions to form the ammonium ion NH_4^+.

$$NH_3 \ + \ H^+ \rightleftharpoons NH_4^+$$

The resulting decline in $[H^+]$ causes more water molecules to ionize. The hydroxide ions remain free in solution while the hydrogen ions react with ammonia molecules.

Similarly, CO_3^{-2} ions remove H^+ ions from the solution, favouring the ionization of more water molecules with an accompanying rise in $[OH^-]$. The hydrogen carbonate ion is formed:

$$CO_3^{-2} \ + \ H^+ \rightleftharpoons HCO_3^-$$

Bases are characterized by electrical conductivity, indicator reactions (litmus and bromothymol both become blue) and a slippery feel.

It is characteristic of both acids and bases that they tend to destroy each other. This is the logical outcome when a solution with a high $[H^+]$ reacts with a solution with a high $[OH^-]$. The ion product $[H^+][OH^-]$ in all cases must be only 10^{-14}.

Acid-Base titrations.

A titration is an experimental procedure by which increasing volumes of a base (or acid) of known concentration are added to a sample containing an unknown quantity of acid (or base) in a beaker or flask.

Initially the solution in the flask has a high $[H^+]$ and a low $[OH^-]$. As base is added some of the hydrogen ions are consumed. When sufficient base has been added the concentration of the hydrogen ions will be reduced so that it is equal to the concentration of the hydroxide ions and the acid is neutralized. Addition of more base will cause the hydroxide ion concentration to exceed the hydrogen ion concentration.

$$H_2O \rightleftharpoons H^+ + OH^-$$

Example: Hydrogen chloride gas is bubbled into one litre of solution, originally 1.00 M sodium hydroxide. Calculate the hydrogen ion concentration after the addition of

(a) 0.10 moles
(b) 0.99 moles
(c) 1.00 moles
(d) 1.01 moles of hydrogen chloride.

Solution: (a) After addition of 0.10 moles H^+, $[OH^-]$ = 0.90 M

$$[H^+] \, [OH^-] = 1.0 \times 10^{-14}$$
$$[H^+] \, 0.9 = 1.0 \times 10^{-14}$$
$$\therefore [H^+] = 1.1 \times 10^{-14} \text{ moles/litre.}$$

(b) After addition of 0.99 moles H^+, $[OH^-]$ = 0.01 M

$$[H^+] \, [OH^-] = 1.0 \times 10^{-14}$$
$$[H^+] \times 10^{-2} = 1.0 \times 10^{-14}$$
$$[H^+] = 1.0 \times 10^{-12} \text{ moles/litre}$$

(c) After addition of 1.00 moles H^+, 1 mole or 17 gm of hydroxide ions will have reacted with 1 mole or 1 gm of hydrogen ions.

$$[OH^-] = [H^+] = 1 \times 10^{-7} \text{ moles per litre}$$

(d) After the addition of 1.01 moles of H^+,

$$[H^+] = 1.01 - 1.00 = 0.01 = 10^{-2} \text{ moles per litre}$$

The answers of (b) and (d) indicate that the addition of only 0.02 moles of HCl change $[H^+]$ by a factor of 10^{10}. The total volume of acid required to produce this sharp change in $[H^+]$ is readily measured with the use of an indicator which changes colour as $[H^+]$ changes markedly.

The "pH of a solution" is a concept which is sometimes encount-
in the study of acids and bases. The letters may be considered to
represent approximately "potential hydrogen" or "presence of hydrogen ion". The definition: pH is the negative of the logarithm of the
hydrogen ion concentration.

Example: Calculate the pH of solutions which are

(a) 0.1 M HCl
(b) 0.01 M HCl
(c) 0.1 M NaOH

Solution: (a) $[H^+] = 0.1 = 10^{-1}$ moles/litre

$$\log [H^+] = \log 10^{-1} = -1$$

$$pH = -\log [H^+] = - (\log 10^{-1}) = -(-1) = 1$$

(b) $[H^+] = 10^{-2}$ moles/litre

$$pH = -\log [H^+] = - (\log 10^{-2}) = -(-2) = 2$$

(c) $[OH^-] = 10^{-1}$ $\therefore$ $[H^+] = \dfrac{10^{-14}}{10^{-1}} = 10^{-13}$ moles/litre

$$pH = -\log [H^+] = - (\log 10^{-13}) = -(-13) = 13$$

Just as a first magnitude star is brighter than a second magnitude
star, a solution of pH = 1 is more acidic than a solution of pH = 2.

Ionization of weak acids

A weak acid is one which partially ionizes. When dissolved in
aqueous solution a state of equilibrium is established. If the general
formula for the acid is HA, then the equilibrium situation is represented

$$HA \rightleftharpoons H^+ + A^-$$

The equilibrium constant for the system

$$K = \frac{[H^+] [A^-]}{[HA]}$$

If the acid is relatively strong, then the numerator will be large, the
denominator will be small and K will be large. Conversely, for a
weak acid, K will be small because the numerator is small and the
denominator is large.

The equilibrium constant for an acid, K_A is readily measured experimentally. This is done by dissolving a known weight of acid

in a known volume of water and measuring the hydrogen ion concentration using acid-base indicators. If the acid is of the general type HA, then the concentration of the anion A^- will equal $[H^+]$.

Example: When 0.1 moles of an acid are dissolved in 1 litre of water the hydrogen ion concentration becomes 1×10^{-4} moles per litre. Assuming that the ionization of each molecule yields only one hydrogen ion, calculate the equilibrium constant K_A for the acid.

Solution: $$HA \rightleftharpoons H^+ + A^-$$

Because $[HA]$ is approximately 10^3 greater than $[H^+]$ and because $[HA]$ is known to 1 significant figure only, assume that

$$[HA] = 0.1 \text{ moles per litre after ionization}$$

$$[H^+] = 10^{-4}M = [A^-]$$

$$\therefore K_A = \frac{[H^+][A^-]}{[HA]} = \frac{10^{-4} \times 10^{-4}}{10^{-1}} = 10^{-7}$$

Example 2: 16 gm of sodium acetate (0.2 moles) are dissolved in 1 litre of 0.1 M acetic acid. Given that $K_A = 1.8 \times 10^{-5}$ for acetic acid, find the hydrogen ion concentration of

(a) 0.1 M acetic acid solution
(b) the final solution.

Solution: $$CH_3COOH \rightleftharpoons CH_3COO^- + H^+$$

$$K_A = \frac{[H^+][CH_3COO^-]}{[CH_3COOH]}$$

(a) Before the sodium acetate was added

$$K_A [CH_3COOH] = [H^+][CH_3COO^-]$$

but $\because [H^+] = [CH_3COO^-]$

$$\therefore K_A [CH_3COOH] = [H^+]^2$$

and $[H^+] = \sqrt{K_A [CH_3COOH]}$

$$= \sqrt{(1.8 \times 10^{-5} \times (10^{-1})}$$

$$= 1.3 \times 10^{-3} M$$

(b) After the sodium acetate was added, the acetate ion concentration rose to slightly above 0.2 molar, the acetic acid concentration remained almost 0.1 molar.

$$[H^+] = \frac{K_A \ [CH_3COOH]}{[CH_3COO^-]}$$

$$= \frac{1.8 \times 10^{-5} \times 10^{-1}}{2 \times 10^{-1}} = 0.9 \times 10^{-5}$$

∴ concentration of hydrogen ion = 9×10^{-6} M. Thus, as could be predicted by Le Chatelier's Principle, the addition of the acetate anion favours the acetate consuming reaction with an accompanying drop in $[H^+]$.

Competition for protons among weak acids — When an acid yields a proton, H^+, to a base in an equilibrium system, the product has a proton which it may donate it a later reaction. That is, by accepting the proton the base has itself been converted to an acid. Similarly the acid residue is capable of accepting a proton and is therefore a base.

For example, $Acid_1 + Base_1 \rightleftharpoons Acid_2 + Base_2$

$$CH_3COOH + NH_3 \rightleftharpoons NH_4^+ + CH_3COO^-$$

By accepting the proton, ammonia forms an acid, NH_4^+ capable of releasing a proton. By releasing the proton the acetic acid forms a base, the acetate ion, which is capable of accepting a proton. Similarly, the acid NH_4^+ forms a base when it releases a proton.

In actual practice it is highly unlikely that protons move alone through aqueous solutions. They tend to get attached to one or more water molecules forming a more stable, larger complex ion. "Hydronium ion" is the name given to the structure formed when a proton unites with a water molecule; the formula is H_3O^+. Generally, the convention is to continue to represent protons in aqueous solution by H^+, with the implicit understanding that the proton is hydrated.

Thus acids and bases may be defined in terms of what they do (characteristic properties) or they may be defined in terms of how they are constructed (whether they are built to release or receive protons).

A substance such as water has the properties of both acids and bases in the latter sense.

Releasing protons: $H_2O \rightleftharpoons H^+ + OH^-$

Accepting protons: $H_2O + H^+ \rightleftharpoons H_3O^+$

Experimentally, the hydrogen ion concentration of a solution may be measured using an electrical device called a pH meter or by the use of acid-base indicators. Each acid-base indicator has a fairly definite value of pH at which it changes colour: by trial an indicator may sometimes be found which shows the intermediate or transition shades when in the solution. Frequently the pH and hence [H^+] are found by establishing that the solution is sufficiently acidic to cause a colour change in Indicator A, but not acidic enough to cause a colour change in Indicator B. (For example, indicator A might be one which changes colour at pH = 4; indicator B. might be one which changes colour at pH = 3. The hydrogen ion concentration then is greater than $10^{-4}M$ yet less than $10^{-3}M$).

A quantitative calculation of the concentration of an acid or a base (rather than just H^+ or OH^- ions) involves the use of titration techniques. Generally, variable amounts of a solution of known concentration are added to the solution of unknown concentration using a burette. The burette is in effect a graduated cylinder with a valve at the bottom which permits the solution to be withdrawn slowly or quickly, as the operator judges.

Example: In a typical case, the known solution is 1.00 molar HCl which can be made up from carefully prepared standard samples which are available commercially. The unknown solution contains sodium hydroxide as the only basic solute. 40.0 mls of acid are used to neutralize 100 mls of the basic solution. What is the molarity of the basic solution?

Solution: $$HCl + NaOH \longrightarrow H_2O + NaCl$$

The number of moles of acid which react must equal the number of moles of base which react.

40.0 ml of 1.00 M acid have $\dfrac{40.0}{1000} \times 1.00 = 0.0400$ moles of HCl.

∴ the 100 ml of base must have contained 0.0400 moles of NaOH.
0.100 l of base has 0.0400 moles of NaOH
1 l of base has 10 times as much, or 0.400 moles of NaOH.
∴ the base is 0.400 M.

Example 2: It is found that 30.0 mls of sulphuric acid, H_2SO_4, of unknown concentration require the addition of 45.0 ml of the 0.400 M NaOH. Find the molarity of the sulphuric acid.

Solution: $$2NaOH + H_2SO_4 \longrightarrow Na_2SO_4 + 2H_2O$$

One mole of H_2SO_4 is able to consume 2 moles of NaOH
45.0 mls of 0.400 M NaOH contain

$$\frac{45.0}{1000} \times 0.400 = 1.80 \times 10^{-2} \text{ moles NaOH}$$

The equation indicates that every mole of NaOH reacts with one half of a mole of H_2SO_4.

∴ 1.80 × 10^{-2} moles NaOH consume $\dfrac{1.80 \times 10^{-2}}{2}$ moles H_2SO_4

= 9.0 × 10^{-3} moles H_2SO_4.

0.0300 litre of acid contain 9.0 × 10^{-3} moles H_2SO_4

∴ 1 litre of acid has $\dfrac{9.0 \times 10^{-3}}{3.0 \times 10^{-2}}$ = 0.30 moles H_2SO_4.

∴ the concentration of the acid solution is 0.30M. In practice this solution would likely not be used as a standard because the measured value is the result of two titration experiments, each of which would have some error associated with it. In analytical work, only the most carefully prepared solutions are taken as standards.

In these calculations answers are generally carried to 3 significant figures because this is the degree of accuracy indicated by the measurements. Note that halving a quantity tends to decrease the degree of accuracy as indicated by the number of significant figures, just as the operation of subtraction tends to decrease the accuracy of approximate or measured numbers. For example, subtraction of a fairly precise quantity 2.345 metres from an equally precise quantity 2.346 metres, yields a fairly imprecise quantity 0.001 metres or 1 millimetre.

UNIT 7

OXIDATION-REDUCTION REACTIONS

These are reactions in which electrons are transferred from one substance to another. For example, when a piece of metallic copper is placed in an aqueous solution of silver nitrate, (colourless), the copper becomes coated with silvery grey crystals and the solution becomes blue. This indicates that:

(a) silver ions are gaining electrons and are being reduced, as shown: $Ag^+ + 1e^- \longrightarrow Ag$

(b) copper atoms are loosing electrons, and are being oxidized, as shown: $Cu \longrightarrow Cu^{+2} + 2e^-$

Neither of these reactions can proceed very far without the other, for this would result in a great surplus (or deficit) of electrons characteristic of electrostatic generators but not of simple chemical reactions.

Just as a Bunsen burner will continue to support a flame if the barrel is unscrewed from and raised above the base, silver ions and copper atoms will react even if they are not in direct contact. This may be investigated as follows: place two beakers side by side: place a solution of silver nitrate, $AgNO_3$, in one and a solution of copper sulphate, $CuSO_4$, in the other; place a silver wire in the beaker of $AgNO_3$ solution and a copper wire in the beaker of $CuSO_4$ solution; join the electrodes together with electrical conductors and use a galvanometer to see if any electron transfer occurs between the two beakers. There will be no detectable electron flow through the meter.

Explanation:

Copper is more reactive than silver. This means that copper atoms have a greater tendency to loose electrons than do silver atoms. Conversely, copper ions have a smaller tendency to gain electrons than do silver ions. When the beaker containing Cu atoms and Cu^{+2} ions is joined to the beaker with Ag atoms and Ag^+ ions, there is a tendency for the Ag^+ ions to deposit on the Ag wire with the absorption of electrons from the wire. These electrons are attracted through the conductor from the copper electrode which can generate electrons as the copper atoms dissolve forming Cu^{+2} ions.

$$Cu \longrightarrow Cu^{+2} + 2e^-$$

All these events happen on a very limited scale when the two electrodes are joined. The reaction stops virtually immediately however because in one beaker (the one with $AgNO_3$ solution) cations only are being removed from the solution, and in the other beaker, (the one with $CuSO_4$ solution) cations only are being added to the solution. To prevent this charge build up which halts the reaction, the two beakers should be joined together by an inverted U tube of an aqueous solution of a salt such as potassium chloride, KCl. Such a tube is called a salt bridge: it allows cations to flow from one beaker to the other, (Figure 7-1).

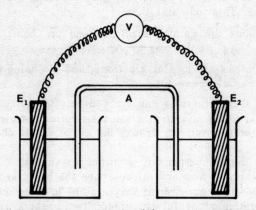

Fig. 7-1 The use of a salt bridge (A) to permit the flow of ions between the beakers. E_1 and E_2 represent the electrodes.

Each copper atom which reacts releases 2 electrons and these two electrons, after being transmitted through the conducting wire will cause the reduction and deposition of 2 atoms of silver. The overall reaction is:

$$Cu + 2Ag^+ \longrightarrow Cu^{+2} + 2Ag$$

This is the sum of two "half-reactions" which are occuring simultaneously. $Cu \longrightarrow Cu^{+2} + 2e^-$

$$2Ag^+ + 2e^- \longrightarrow 2Ag$$

The coefficients in the last equation have been doubled because all electrons released by the copper are used to reduce the silver, maintaining electrical neutrality.

A "half-cell" is a metal electrode dipping into a solution of a salt of that metal. An electrochemical cell is two different half-cells joined together; the equation for the overall cell reaction is the sum of the "half-reactions" or the equations for the reactions which occur in the half-cells. The number of electrons consumed in the reduction reaction must equal the number of electrons generated in the oxidation reaction and accordingly electrons are not shown in the equation for the overall reaction.

Oxidation – the half-reaction in which electrons are lost.

Examples:
$$Na \longrightarrow Na^+ + 1e^-$$
$$Mg \longrightarrow Mg^{+2} + 2e^-$$
$$Al \longrightarrow Al^{+3} + 3e^-$$

Reduction – the half-reaction in which electrons are gained.

Examples:
$$Al^{+3} + 3e^- \longrightarrow Al$$
$$Mg^{+2} + 2e^- \longrightarrow Mg$$
$$Cu^{+2} + 2e^- \longrightarrow Cu$$

When zinc metal (which is more reactive than copper) is dropped into a beaker of aqueous copper sulphate the half reactions which occur are:

oxidation $\quad Zn \longrightarrow Zn^{+2} + 2e^-$

reduction $\quad Cu^{+2} + 2e^- \longrightarrow Cu$

The overall reaction is: $Zn + Cu^{+2} \longrightarrow Zn^{+2} + Cu$

This reaction is reversible, as are all chemical reactions, but the state of equilibrium favours the products on the right so strongly that for most purposes the reaction is complete.

In some cases the ions involved have approximately similar attracting abilities for electrons and the existence of an equilibrium state becomes apparent. Two ions which illustrate this possibility are those of cobalt and nickel. When metallic cobalt is placed in aqueous nickel (II) sulphate, the cobalt is oxidized and the nickel is reduced.

$$Co \longrightarrow Co^{+2} + 2e^-$$
$$Ni^{+2} + 2e^- \longrightarrow Ni$$

As the concentration of the Co^{+2} ion rises, the rate of reduction to metallic cobalt tends to increase, returning Ni^{+2} ions to the solution. At equilibrium there are approximately equal concentrations of the two ions.

$$Co + Ni^{+2} \rightleftharpoons Co^{+2} + Ni$$

Metals which have similar activity will tend to form ions which have similar attracting power for electrons. Aqueous solutions of these ions will form readily detectable equilibrium systems with the elementary forms of the metals. Metals of widely different activity, such as zinc and copper, will not tend to form significant equilibrium systems with a solution containing the ions of the metals.

Nomenclature of an Electrochemical Cell

Anode — The electrical conductor at which oxidation occurs. The electrons released by the oxidation flow from the anode to the external circuit. A typical anode reaction:

$$Zn \longrightarrow Zn^{+2} + 2e^-$$

Cathode — The electrical conductor at which reduction occurs. The electrons which are used in the reduction are delivered to the cathode by an electromagnetic generator or a chemical half-cell. A typical cathode reduction reaction:

$$Ag^+ + 1e^- \longrightarrow Ag$$

ELECTRON TRANSFER AND THE PREDICTION OF REACTIONS —

In any cell electrons are released by oxidation at the anode and these electrons flow to the cathode to permit the reduction reaction. (If the connection is broken both reactions must stop). Any flow of electrons can be made to do work or to release energy: the amount of work which can be done by the average electron is indicated by the voltage of the source of electron flow. If the voltage of the current source doubles, then the amount of work done by an average electron doubles. If the voltage of the current triples, then the amount of energy per electron triples. That is, the electron energy varies directly as voltage; conversely the voltage of the source is directly proportional to the amount of work done per electron.

1 volt is equivalent to 1 joule of work being done by each coulomb of flowing electrons; i.e., 0.24 calories of energy per 6.2×10^{18} electrons. A potential difference between two electrodes of 1 volt means that one electron releases $\dfrac{0.24}{6.2 \times 10^{18}} = 3.8 \times 10^{-20}$ calories when it flows between the two terminals.

Just as the overall reaction for a cell is the sum of the individual half-cell reactions, the overall voltage (or energy transfer per electron) is the sum of voltages of each half cell.

Measuring Half-Cell Potentials — Altitudes and elevations on the earth's surface are measured relative to an arbitrary standard, such as sea level, which is set at zero. The amount of energy transferred per electron by a particular half-cell is found by connecting that half-cell to a standard half-cell which is arbitrarily assigned zero voltage. The potential difference between the two is then measured with a voltmeter.

The resulting experimental value, called the half-cell electrode potential, is the amount of energy transferred per electron and is represented by the symbol E°.

The standard half-cell process which has a chosen voltage of zero is that in which hydrogen gas is bubbled into an aqueous solution of an acid.

$$H_2 \rightleftharpoons 2H^+ + 2e^-$$

If two hydrogen half-cells were connected by a salt bridge and electrical conductors, there would be no current and no voltage because identical electrodes can not produce a current. (Recall that identical atoms tend to form molecules rather than ions; neither atom has sufficiently great attracting power to remove an electron from the other, e.g. O_2). By definition then, for the hydrogen half-cell, $E^\circ = 0.00$ volts.

When a hydrogen half-cell is connected to a zinc-zinc sulphate half-cell, experiment indicates that E° for the Zn-Zn^{+2} oxidation reaction is $E^\circ = +0.76$ volts. This is what happens: at the anode atoms of zinc are oxidized:

$$Zn \longrightarrow Zn^{+2} + 2e^-$$

at the cathode ions of hydrogen are reduced:

$$2H^+ + 2\bar{e} \longrightarrow H_2 \uparrow$$

The electrons released by the zinc are ultimately incorporated into the molecules of the hydrogen gas which bubble away from the hydrogen electrode. In transit through the conductor, each electron can release approximately 2.9×10^{-20} calories.

When a hydrogen half-cell is connected to a copper-copper sulphate half-cell the cell voltage is found to be 0.34 volts. In this case however, the hydrogen electrode is the anode. This is because hydrogen is more reactive than copper; hydrogen ions have less ability to attract electrons than copper ions. If electrons are available for either Cu^{+2} or H^+ ions, the copper will generally take them.

At the hydrogen electrode, oxidation occurs: $H_2 \longrightarrow 2H^+ + 2e^-$

At the Cu-Cu^{+2} electrode, reduction occurs: $Cu^{+2} + 2e^- \longrightarrow Cu$

To indicate that the electrons are flowing away from the hydrogen electrode, the electrode potential for the Cu-Cu^{+2} half-cell reaction is written with a negative sign:

$$E^\circ = -0.34 \text{ volts.}$$

Similarly, a positive value for E° for a half-cell indicates that the half-cell has a greater tendency to generate electrons than the H_2-$2H^+$ half-cell: such a half-cell would send electrons to a H_2-$2H^+$ half-cell.

For uniformity in reporting experimental results in this field measurements are made with all substances in their "standard states".

The chosen standard states are:

(a) for gases, 1 atmosphere and 25°C

(b) for ions, a 1 Molar solution i.e. 1 mole of the ion per litre.

(c) for pure substances, the pure form at 25°C.

The standard oxidation potential, $E°$, for the half-cell of almost any metal in contact with its ions may be found by consulting a table of standard half-cell potentials. For uniformity, all the half-reactions shown in such a table are for the oxidation process. In an actual cell reduction occurs at the cathode and the change which occurs at the cathode is the exact opposite of that shown in the oxidation equation for the element.

Example: A $Zn-Zn^{+2}$ half-cell, $E° = +0.76$ volts, is connected to a $Cu-Cu^{+2}$ half-cell, $E° = -0.34$ volts. Which way will the electrons flow in the circuit and what is the voltage of the cell?

Solution: The $Zn-Zn^{+2}$ half-cell can deliver electrons to a hydrogen half-cell with a potential of 0.76 volts or 2.9×10^{-20} calories per electron. A $Cu-Cu^{+2}$ half-cell can draw electrons from a hydrogen half-cell with a potential of 0.34 volts or 1.3×10^{-20} calories per electron. Recalling that an ocean trench 5 miles deep is 9 miles beneath a 4 mile high mountain, it seems logical that a $Cu-Cu^{+2}$ half-cell draws electrons from a $Zn-Zn^{+2}$ half-cell with a potential of 0.76 plus 0.34 = 1.10 volts or approximately 4.2×10^{-20} calories per electron. The electrons will flow from the zinc electrode to the copper electrode because the more active metal reacts by releasing electrons.

The voltage generated by the reaction of zinc metal with copper (II) ions is therefore +1.10 volts; the positive value indicates that energy is being released from the system.

NOTE: What has happened in this case illustrates a general rule for finding cell potentials. The overall cell potential is the sum of the two half-cell potentials:

E total = E oxidation of Zn to Zn^{+2} + E reduction of Cu^{+2} to Cu

The voltage for the reduction of Cu^{+2} to Cu is the exact opposite of the voltage for the oxidation of Cu to Cu^{+2}, i.e. the opposite of $E°$ $(Cu-Cu^{+2})$

$$\therefore E_{total} = E°(Zn-Zn^{+2}) - E° (Cu-Cu^{+2})$$

$$= 0.76 - (-0.34)$$

$$= + 1.10 \text{ volts}$$

Example: The standard electrode potential $E°$ for a half-cell containing elementary cobalt in contact with a $1M$. solution of Co^{+2} ions is +0.28 volts. What voltage will be produced when this half-cell is connected to a $Zn-Zn^{+2}$ half-cell of $E° = 0.76$ volts?

Solution I:

The oxidation of the zinc releases 2.9×10^{-20} calories per electron; the oxidation of the cobalt releases 1.1×10^{-20} calories per electron. Because randomness effects are approximately the same, the process which releases more energy (leaving the substances in lower energy states) is favoured.

In this case the oxidation of the elementary zinc proceeds. Each released electron has 2.9×10^{-20} calories of energy. The cobalt-cobalt ion half-cell is forced to run backwards. The energy required to do this, 1.1×10^{-20} calories per electron transferred, must be supplied by the electrons released by the zinc. Each electron released by the zinc as it reacts has 2.9×10^{-20} calories of energy; 1.1×10^{-20} calories of this energy are used to drive the reduction reaction:

$$Co^{+2} + 2e^- \longrightarrow Co \quad (+0.28 \text{ volt})$$

Each electron then has approximately $(2.9 - 1.1) \times 10^{-20} = 1.8 \times 10^{-20}$ calories of energy which may be released as heat in the external circuit. This corresponds to a potential difference between the electrodes of approximately 0.11 calories per coulomb or half a volt.

Solution 2:

This method is more direct. The general formula is:

$$E_{\text{cell}} = E_1^° - E_2^°$$

where: $E_2^°$ is the electrode oxidation potential of the half-cell with the greater tendency to proceed.

$E_1^°$ is the electrode oxidation potential of the half-cell with the smaller tendency to proceed. This is the cell in which reduction is occurring (or the oxidation process is being run backwards). In this case:

$$E_1^° = E° (Zn-Zn^{+2}) = +0.76 \text{ volts}$$
$$E_2^° = E° (Co-Co^{+2}) = +0.28 \text{ volts}$$
$$E_{\text{cell}} = +0.76 - (+0.28) = +0.48 \text{ volts}$$

If the $Co-Co^{+2}$ half-cell were replaced with a hydrogen half-cell or a $Cu-Cu^{+2}$ half-cell in which reduction occurs more readily, then the value of the cell voltage would increase.

Example: The electrode potential for the oxidation of zinc is $+0.76$ volts; the electrode potential for the oxidation of silver is E° (Ag – Ag$^+$) = -0.80 volt. Write the equation for the overall reaction and calculate the voltage developed by the cell formed by joining these two half-cells.

Solution: The large E° for the Zn-Zn^{+2} half-cell indicates that oxidation will occur in this half-cell because zinc atoms have a great tendency to lose electrons.

$$Zn \longrightarrow Zn^{+2} + 2e^- \qquad E^\circ = +0.76 \text{ volt}$$

Each ionization releases 2 electrons, each one of which will cause the reduction of 1 silver ion. To maintain electrical neutrality, two silver ions must be reduced for each zinc atom oxidized.

$$2Ag^{+1} + 2e^- \longrightarrow 2Ag$$

This reduction equation is true, but it is not given in any list of oxidation reactions. To avoid confusion, an accepted convention when dealing with the reversible reactions of electrochemistry is to consider any reduction the exact opposite of an oxidation. The reduction of silver ions may then be written:

$$-(2Ag \longrightarrow 2Ag^{+1} + 2e^-) \qquad -E^\circ = -(-0.80 \text{ volt})$$

Summing the equations:

$$
\begin{array}{lll}
Zn \longrightarrow Zn^{+2} + 2e^- & +0.76 \text{ volts} \\
-2Ag \longrightarrow -2Ag^+ - 2e^- & +0.80 \text{ volts} \\
\hline
Zn - 2Ag \longrightarrow Zn^{+2} - 2Ag^+ & +1.56 \text{ volts}
\end{array}
$$

On rearranging to eliminate the negative signs the final equation becomes:

$$Zn + 2Ag^+ \longrightarrow Zn^{+2} + 2Ag$$

$$E_{cell} = +1.56 \text{ volts}$$

Note that when a half-cell equation is doubled or tripled, the value of E° is unchanged. This is because E° is a ratio of (quantity of energy)/(electron moving through the circuit) and the value of E° is independent of the number of electrons which actually flow. (A heat of reaction of 150 kilocalories per mole is not doubled by doubling the equation, nor is a gasoline consumption of 25 miles per gallon changed by altering the length of the trip).

The treatment to this point has been concerned with cells composed of two half-cells linked by a salt bridge and electrical conductors. The purpose of this approach is to emphasize that there are two distinct reactions proceeding, each one dependent on the other. In practice, a complete cell may be made by placing two different metals in a solution of an appropriate electrolyte and connecting the metal electrodes to an external circuit. The metal with the higher oxidation potential will become oxidized and release electrons to the external circuit. These electrons will then be used to complete the reduction of the ions of the less active metal which are in the same solution.

Predicting Reactions from Half-cell Potentials

Example 1: The oxidation potential of cobalt is $+0.28$ volts. Will elementary cobalt dissolve when placed in an acid solution which is $1.0\ M$ with respect to hydrogen ions?

Solution: If the cobalt is to react, then it must be oxidized as shown

$$Co \longrightarrow Co^{+2} + 2e^- \qquad E^\circ = +0.28 \text{ volts}$$

The hydrogen must accordingly be reduced. The equation is the reverse of the hydrogen oxidation equation.

$$- (H_2 \longrightarrow 2H^+ + 2e^-) \qquad -E^\circ = 0.00 \text{ volts}$$

Adding these two:

$$Co - H_2 \longrightarrow Co^{+2} - 2H^+$$

or

$$Co + 2H^+ \longrightarrow Co^{+2} + H_2 \uparrow \quad E^\circ = +0.28 \text{ volts}$$

The positive value of E° indicates that energy is released in this reaction and that the reaction is favoured by energy considerations.

Example 2: A sample of silver is placed in an acidic solution which has $[H^+] = 1.0\ M$. Will the silver react?

$$E^\circ\ (Ag - Ag^+) = -0.80 \text{ volts}.$$

Solution: If the silver is to react it must be oxidized:

$$Ag \longrightarrow Ag^+ + 1e^- \qquad E^\circ = -0.80 \text{ volts}$$

The hydrogen must be reduced:

$$- (H_2 \longrightarrow 2H^+ + 2e^-) \quad - E^\circ = 0.00 \text{ volts}$$

To maintain electrical neutrality, the equation for the oxidation of the silver must be doubled.

$$2\,Ag \longrightarrow 2Ag^+ + 2e^- \qquad -0.80 \text{ volts}$$

$$-H_2 \longrightarrow -2H^+ \quad -2e^- \qquad 0.00 \text{ volts}$$

or

$$2Ag - H_2 \longrightarrow 2Ag^+ - 2H^+ \qquad -0.80 \text{ volts}$$

$$2Ag + 2H^+ \rightleftharpoons 2Ag^+ + H_2\uparrow \qquad E^\circ = -0.80 \text{ volts}$$

The large negative value of E° indicates that considerable energy must be supplied to this system to make the reaction proceed. Because of these energy considerations elementary silver does not react with hydrogen ions significantly: the state of equilibrium very strongly favours the low energy reactants Ag and H^+. The silver can be made to react with the acid more perceptibly by removing almost all silver ions from the solution, thereby minimizing the reverse reaction. The silver ions may be removed by precipitating them as the very low solubility salt silver iodide, AgI.

Predictions based on E° values must be confirmed experimentally if they are to be used seriously. In general, if the proposed reaction has a fairly negative E°, then energy considerations favour the reactants but there will likely be at least a trace of products. If the proposed reaction has a positive E°, then energy considerations favour the products but the reaction may be one whose mechanisim causes a low rate: i.e. a long time is required to reach the state of equilibrium. If the proposed reaction has a slightly negative E°, then predictions are not reliable, especially if the substances are not in their standard states.

For example, zinc metal reacts with a solution which is 1.0 Molar with respect to both Zn^{+2} and Ni^{+2}, E° (Zn-Zn^{+2}) = +0.76 volts, E° (Ni-Ni^{+2}) = +0.25 volts. The nickel (II) ions are reduced.

$$Zn \rightleftharpoons Zn^{+2} + 2e^- \qquad 0.76 \text{ volts}$$

$$-(Ni \rightleftharpoons Ni^{+2} + 2e^-) \qquad -(0.25 \text{ volts})$$

or

$$Zn - Ni \rightleftharpoons Zn^{+2} - Ni^{+2} \qquad 0.51 \text{ volt}$$

$$Zn + Ni^{+2} \rightleftharpoons Zn^{+2} + Ni \qquad E^\circ = +0.51 \text{ volts}$$

The positive value of E° indicates that the zinc will react. The rate of consumption of zinc may be increased by placing the zinc in a solution which has only nickel ions initially present. In this case, the departure from standard conditions speeds the disappearance of the zinc because the reverse reaction is minimized.

Oxidation Numbers.

Because oxidation means the loss of electrons, an atom which is being oxidized is becoming more positive. The extent of the charge on an atom of an element is indicated by the oxidation number of the element, ON. The charge may be real, as in the case of a single ion, or hypothetical, as in the case of atoms in molecules or compound ions.

Calculating Oxidation Numbers.

(a) The oxidation number of uncombined elements is zero.

(b) The oxidation number of an element in a compound is usually the charge on the ions of that element. For example, for hydrogen in H_2SO_4 or H_2O, ON = +1, for oxygen in H_2SO_4 or K_2O, ON = -2, for potassium in K_2O or KI, ON = +1.

(c) Because oxidation numbers are indicating a degree of charge, the sum of the oxidation numbers of all atoms in a molecule (which must be neutral) must be zero.

Example: What is the ON for sulphur in H_2SO_4?

Solution: The total oxidation number for hydrogen is $2 \times (+1) = +2$. The total oxidation number for oxygen is $4 \times (-2) = -8$. To ensure neutrality the sulphur atom must have an ON which brings the sum of the total oxidation numbers to zero. The oxidation number for sulphur in H_2SO_4 is +6.

(d) The sum of the oxidation numbers of the atoms in a compound ion equals the charge on the ion.

Example: What is the oxidation number of phosphorus in the phosphate ion PO_4^{-3}?

Solution: The four oxygen atoms have a total oxidation number of -8. The ion has a charge of -3. The phosphorus atom must have an oxidation number of +5.

Oxidation is often defined as an increase in oxidation number. In the following example sulphur is oxidized as its ON changes from 0 to 4.

$$S + O_2 \longrightarrow SO_2$$

Reduction is a decrease in oxidation number. The oxidation number becomes less positive or more negative. In the above equation, the oxygen is reduced as the ON changes from O to -2.

Balancing of Oxidation – Reduction Reactions.

(a) By electrons. This is readily done when it is remembered that
  (i) matter must be conserved
  (ii) all electrons released by the oxidation must be consumed by the reduction.

If the oxidation half-reaction releases X electrons and if the reduction half-reaction uses Y electrons, then the overall equation is the sum of Y times the oxidation equation plus X times the reduction equation.

Example: Find the overall equation when permanganate ions oxidize hydrogen sulphide.

Reduction reaction: $MnO_4^- + 8H^+ + 5e^- \longrightarrow Mn^{+2} + 4H_2O$ (Y=5)

Oxidation reaction: $H_2S \longrightarrow S + 2H^+ + 2e^-$ (X=2)

Solution: $2(MnO_4^- + 8H^+ + 5e^- \longrightarrow Mn^{+2} + 4H_2O)$

$5(H_2S \longrightarrow S + 2H^+ + 2e^-)$

$2MnO_4^- + 16H^+ + 10e^- + 5H_2S \longrightarrow 2Mn^{+2} + 8H_2O + 5S + 10H^+ + 10e^-$

or: $2MnO_4^- + 6H^+ + 5 H_2S \longrightarrow 2Mn^{+2} + 5S + 8H_2O$

If any factor is common between X and Y, then this factor should be cancelled out before multiplying the half equations.

Example: Find the overall equation when dichromate ions oxidize tin (II) ions.

Oxidation reaction: $Sn^{+2} \longrightarrow Sn^{+4} + 2e^-$

Reduction reaction: $Cr_2O_7^{-2} + 6e^- + 14H^+ \longrightarrow 2Cr^{+3} + 7H_2O$

Solution: X = 2 and Y = 6. The simplest ratio, found by removing the common factor 2, is X: Y = 1:3. Three tin (II) ions are required to reduce one dichromate ion.

The overall equation is:

or $3 Sn^{+2} + Cr_2O_7^{-2} + 6e^- + 14H^+ \longrightarrow 3Sn^{+4} + 6e^- + 2Cr^{+3} + 7H_2O$

$3 Sn^{+2} + Cr_2O_7^{-2} + 14H^+ \longrightarrow 3 Sn^{+4} + 2Cr^{+3} + 7H_2O$

The electrons released by oxidation of three ions of Sn^{+2} are absorbed during the reduction of 1 ion of $Cr_2O_7^{-2}$.

Balancing of Oxidation-Reduction Reactions —
(b) By oxidation numbers.

The same principles apply in this method. If the solution is to remain neutral, then any increase in total charge by one element must be equal and opposite to the change in total charge of the other element which is having a change in ON.

Example: In the reaction between dichromate and tin (II) ions, each dichromate ion has two chromium atoms; the total oxidation number of chromium decreases from +12 to +6. Each tin ion has a change in ON from +2 to +4. Because the decrease in one ON is 3 times the increase in the other ON, the oxidation reaction must occur three times as frequently as the reduction reaction. We then have the same 3:1 ratio which was found by balancing electrons.

Electrolysis

This is a process by which a reaction which does not proceed spontaneously, because of energy considerations, is forced to occur. This is accomplished by delivering to the reactants electrical energy which was generated by a working chemical cell or by an electro-magnetic generator.

Example: Elementary aluminum is obtained by the electrolysis of a hot, non-aqueous solution containing the dissociated oxide Al_2O_3.

$$\text{at the positive electrode:} \quad O^{-2} \longrightarrow O + 2e^-$$
$$\text{at the negative electrode:} \quad Al^{+3} + 3e \longrightarrow Al$$

As the oxygen is liberated it reacts with the carbon anode; the molten aluminum is collected.

The electrolysis is the reverse of the reaction which tends to proceed spontaneously:

$$4Al + 3O_2 \longrightarrow 2Al_2O_3$$

EXPERIMENTS:

(1) When a reactive metal such as zinc is placed in a solution of copper sulphate, the blue colour fades from the solution and a dark brown solid deposit is formed.

$$Zn + Cu^{+2} \longrightarrow Zn^{+2} + Cu \qquad E^\circ = +1.10 \text{ volt}$$

(2) When chlorine gas is bubbled into aqueous sodium bromide, a reddish brown colour is produced, indicating the production of elementary bromine Br_2.

Explanation: The half-equations for the oxidation of chloride and bromide ions are:

$$2Br^- \longrightarrow 2e^- + Br_2 \qquad E^\circ = -1.06 \text{ volts.}$$
$$2Cl^- \longrightarrow 2e^- + Cl_2 \qquad E^\circ = -1.36 \text{ volts.}$$

The value of E° ($2Br^- - Br_2$) is greater than that of E° ($2Cl^- - Cl_2$), indicating that the bromide ion has a greater tendency to loose electrons than does the chloride ion. The reaction with the greater E° proceeds; the reaction with the lesser E° is run backwards.

$$2Br^- \longrightarrow 2e^- + Br_2 \qquad\qquad -1.06 \text{ volts}$$

$$-(2Cl^- \longrightarrow 2e^- + Cl_2) \qquad -(-1.36 \text{ volts})$$

$$\overline{2Br^- - 2Cl^- \longrightarrow Br_2 - Cl_2 \qquad E^\circ = +0.30 \text{ volts}}$$

or

$$Cl_2 + 2Br^- \longrightarrow Br_2 + 2Cl^-$$

The positive value of E° indicates that the reaction is favoured.

(3) If bromine water is added to an aqueous solution of potassium iodide and if carbon tetrachloride is added, then the carbon tetrachloride will fall to the bottom of the solution and form a violet solution. The presence of the violet colour indicates the release of elementary iodine, I_2.

Explanation: The oxidation equation for iodine is:

$$2 I^- \longrightarrow 2e^- + I_2 \qquad\qquad E^\circ = -0.53 \text{ volts}$$

Because E° $(2 I^- - I_2)$ is greater than E° $(2 Br^- - Br_2)$, the oxidation of iodine will proceed while the oxidation of bromide is reversed. That is, bromine will be reduced.

$$2 I^- \longrightarrow 2e^- + I_2 \qquad\qquad -0.53 \text{ volts.}$$

$$-(2Br^- \longrightarrow 2e^- + Br_2) \qquad -(-1.06) \text{ volts.}$$

$$\overline{2I^- - 2Br^- \longrightarrow I_2 - Br_2 \qquad E^\circ = +0.53 \text{ volts.}}$$

or

$$2I^- + Br_2 \longrightarrow I_2 + 2Br^-$$

(4) If equal volumes of $0.1M$ magnesium nitrate, $Mg(NO_3)_2$, and $0.1M$ sodium hydroxide, NaOH, are mixed, then a white precipitate of magnesium hydroxide $Mg(OH)_2$ forms. This is because the product $[Mg^{+2}] [OH^-]^2$ greatly exceeds the solubility product for $Mg(OH)_2$ which is 9×10^{-12}.

(5) The oxidations of Fe^{+2} and Mn^{+2} are represented by the following:

$$Fe^{+2} \longrightarrow Fe^{+3} + 1e^- \qquad\qquad E^\circ = -0.77 \text{ volt.}$$

$$Mn^{+2} + 4H_2O \longrightarrow 5e^- + MnO_4^- + 8H^+ \qquad E^\circ = -1.52 \text{ volt.}$$

In a solution containing all of these ions, the tendency is for the oxidation of Fe^{+2} to proceed and for the oxidation of Mn^{+2} to reverse. Note that the 5 electrons absorbed by each MnO_4^- ion are released by the oxidation of 5 Fe^{+2} ions.

$$5(Fe^{+2} \longrightarrow Fe^{+3} + 1e^-) \qquad\qquad -0.77 \text{ volt}$$

$$-(Mn^{+2} + 4H_2O \longrightarrow 5e^- + MnO_4^- + 8H^+) \qquad -(-1.52) \text{ volt}$$

$$\overline{5 Fe^{+2} + MnO_4^- + 8H^+ \longrightarrow 5Fe^{+3} + Mn^{+2} + 4H_2O \qquad E^\circ = +0.75 \text{ volts}}$$

The large value of E° indicates that when permanganate ions are added to iron (II) ions the state of equilibrium strongly favours the products. The purple or pink colour of the permanganate will be replaced by the yellow colour usually associated with aqueous solutions of Fe^{+3}.

UNIT 8

EXPERIMENTAL BASIS FOR THE ATOMIC THEORY

The atomic theory as we now understand it has been assembled from fragments of knowledge obtained by the work of thousands of skilled experimental workers in the past 150 years. Some of the experimental observations which strongly suggest the existence of discrete particles of matter are summarized as follows:

(1) The Law of Definite Proportions states that all samples of a particular substance (eg. water) have the same elements (hydrogen and oxygen) in the same proportion by weight (89:11). Similarly all samples of mercury (II) oxide, irregardless of mass, contain 93 weights of mercury for every 7 weights of oxygen. This is consistent with basic building units being repeated an integral number of times.

(2) The Law of Multiple Proportions applies to substances such as mercury (I) oxide and mercury (II) oxide. Mercury (I) oxide may be formed experimentally by reacting 100 gm of mercury with 4 gm of oxygen. Mercury (II) oxide may be formed by reacting 50 gm of mercury with 4 gm of oxygen under different conditions. The Law: if two elements (e.g. mercury and oxygen) form two different compounds, then the two weights of one element (mercury) which combine with an arbitrary or chosen weight of the other element (oxygen) are in the ratio of small integers (100:50 or 2:1). This indicates that if one particle of oxygen combines with X particles of mercury when forming mercury (II) oxide, then one particle of oxygen combines with 2X particles of mercury when forming mercury (I) oxide.

(3) The Law of Combining Gas Volumes states that if two (or more) gases are involved in a chemical reaction, then their volumes are in the ratio of small integers. The only stipulation is that the gas volumes be compared at the same temperature and pressure. For example, two litres of carbon monoxide react with one litre of oxygen to form two litres of carbon dioxide, (all measurements at the same temperature and pressure). This is consistent with the concept that at a particular temperature and pressure the average gas molecule has a certain volume of space about itself. When measuring volumes we are measuring a quantity which is proportional to the number of gas molecules.

No similar, simple law is possible for solids or liquids because the number of molecules per litre varies widely from one substance to another. We now know that 1 litre of any gas at

S.T.P. has $\dfrac{6 \times 10^{23}}{22.4}$ = 3×10^{22} molecules, no matter what gas is considered.

(4) Faraday's laws of electrolysis

(a) A constant current, flowing for a definite period of time, will deposit a definite amount of a particular metal from a solution of one of its salts.

This is consistent with the concept that each ion absorbs a definite quantity of electricity as it is deposited.

(b) A certain quantity of electrical charge, 96,500 coulombs, will deposit $1/n$ moles of metal, where n is the valence of the metal. Thus, 96,500 coulombs will deposit 1 mole of sodium (23gm) or $\frac{1}{2}$ mole of calcium (20gm) or $\frac{1}{3}$ mole of aluminum (9gm). (All these reactions may be done in water-free liquids, generally molten salts).

That is, the deposition of a particle of calcium require twice twice as much electricity as the deposition of a sodium particle. This is consistent with our concepts of bivalent calcium ions and univalent sodium ions. It follows that one mole of electrons has a charge of 96,500 coulombs.

Example: A current of 2 amperes or 2 coulombs per second flows for 50 minutes. Find: (a) the number of coulombs delivered
(b) the weight of copper which could be deposited from a solution of copper (II) sulphate, $CuSO_4$, by this quantity of charge.

Solution:
(a) In 1 second 2 coulombs are delivered. In 50×60 seconds, $2 \times 50 \times 60$ = 6000 coulombs are delivered.

In general, the quantity of charge = Q = It coulombs where I is the current intensity in coulombs/sec or amperes and t is the time in seconds.

(b) The reduction of a copper (II) ion requires 2 electrons. One mole of electrons will be able to reduce $\frac{1}{2}$ mole of Cu^{+2} ions.

96,500 coulombs reduce $\frac{1}{2}$ mole or 32 gm of copper

1 coulomb will reduce 32/96,500 gm of copper

6000 coulombs reduce $\dfrac{32}{96,500} \times 6000$ = 2 gm of copper.

PHYSICAL EVIDENCE FOR THE THE ATOMIC THEORY

When a high potential difference is applied across two electrodes separated by a gas, a flow of positive and negative particles results between the electrodes. Either sparks or coloured streamers result, depending on the gas pressure and the applied voltage.

If the experiment is repeated with the electrodes sealed in an evacuated container, then it is found that invisible "cathode rays" travel from the cathode (negative) to the anode (positive).

The position of these rays is located by placing a screen coated with a fluorescent substance (such as zinc sulphide, ZnS) in the tube. When the cathode rays strike the screen some of their energy is converted to visible light.

Experiments with cathode rays in a variety of vacuum tubes indicate that cathode rays
  (a) may turn a paddle wheel
  (b) may cause a piece of metal to become red hot
  (c) may be deflected by electric and magnetic fields.
The implications are that cathode rays have mass, energy and electric charge. They are in fact high speed electrons.

Experiments with cathode rays tubes yielded neither the value of the electron charge (e) nor the value of the electron mass (m). Cathode ray measurements did show the value of the ratio:

$$e/m = 1.76 \times 10^{11} \text{ coulombs/kilogram}$$

If it were possible to collect 1 kilogram of electrons, then the quantity of charge would be 1.76×10^{11} coulombs. A current of 10 amperes, such as one finds in an operating electric tea kettle, would have to flow for 570 years to deliver this quantity of charge. The intense repulsive forces which would be encountered mean that the accumulation of 1 kilogram (or even 1 microgram) of pure electrons is a highly unlikely event.

The magnitude of the charge on an individual electron was measured by Millikan in an experiment with oil drops. Neutral drops in a typical experiment are found to fall with velocities of approximately 0.2 mm/sec; others are attracted towards charged plates with velocities which indicate that the drops have charges such as 1.6×10^{-19} coulombs or 3.2×10^{-19} coulombs or 4.8×10^{-19} coulombs. It is assumed that the smallest charge found on any drop, 1.6×10^{-19} coulomb, is the charge resulting when a neutral drop gains, or looses, one electron.

The mass of an individual electron is then found from e/m to be 9×10^{-31} kgm.

Mass Spectrograph — The principles which describe the motion of electrons in cathode ray tubes may also be applied to the behaviour of positive ions formed when metals are vaporized and ionized. The ions are fed into a velocity filter which removes by electric deflection all ions which do not have a chosen speed v. The remaining ions of speed v are fed into a container in which there are controlled electric and magnetic fields. The ions are deflected into a circular path, the radius of which depends on the ionic mass. By measuring the radius of the circle, the mass of the ion is calculated.

Physical evidence thus gives information about atomic mass and ionic charge which is in agreement with that obtained by chemical techniques. In addition, physical evidence shows the probable arrangement of matter within the individual atom.

A classical experiment in this field is one in which small projectiles are fired at a thin sheet of matter. The projectiles are helium nuclei or $\propto$-particles, He^{+2}, and the target is a thin sheet of gold a few hundred atoms thick. The majority of $\propto$-particles pass through the sheet without deflection, indicating that the sheet is mainly empty space. About one particle in 10,000 deflects back in the general direction of the $\propto$-particle source. Calculations based on the measured deflections indicate that very small particles in the foil with highly concentrated electrical charges are responsible for the deflection. The effect is similar to that obtained when a handful of sand is thrown at a wire fence — most particles pass through, but some are deflected; in the case of nuclei, no actual contact is made.

The development of the nuclear model of the atom (dense, positive nucleus with 99.9% of the matter, surrounded by highly mobile electrons) was a result of the experiments with $\propto$-particles.

INFORMATION ABOUT ATOMIC AND MOLECULAR DIMENSIONS FROM LIGHT

Sound waves are a means of sending energy, with no transfer of matter, from one region to another. They travel through a given medium with a characteristic speed and obey the equation

$$v = n\lambda$$

where v is the speed of propagation, n is the frequency (the number of waves produced per second) and λ is the wave length (the total length of one condensation and one rarefaction).

The human ear can hear sounds of some but not all frequencies.

Light is also a wave disturbance which obeys the wave equation

$$v = n\lambda \qquad \text{or} \qquad c = \nu\lambda$$

where c is the speed of light (3×10^5 km/sec in air) and ν (nu) is the frequency of the light source.

Example: Calculate the wave length of violet light ($\nu = 7.5 \times 10^{14}$ waves/sec) and of red light ($\nu = 4.3 \times 10^{14}$ waves/sec).

Solution: Violet light:
$$\lambda = \frac{c}{\nu} = \frac{3 \times 10^{10}}{7.5 \times 10^{14}} \frac{\text{cm/sec.}}{\text{waves/sec.}}$$

$$= 4 \times 10^{-5} \text{ cm/wave}$$

$$\text{Red light:} \qquad \lambda = \frac{c}{\nu} = \frac{3 \times 10^{10}}{4.3 \times 10^{14}} \frac{\text{cm/sec}}{\text{waves/sec.}}$$

$$\lambda = 7 \times 10^{-5} \text{ cm/wave.}$$

Radiation of wavelength less than 4×10^{-5} cm, or 4000 Angstroms, is invisible. If the radiation has wavelength between 4000 and 150 Angstroms, then it is called ultraviolet radiation. If the radiation has wave length between 150 and 0.1 Angstroms, then it is called X-radiation.

By using visible light it is possible to calculate the width of a slit by passing light of a known wavelength through the slit and measuring the interference and diffraction pattern which results.

Similarly, by using X-rays, it is possible to measure the separation of atoms in a crystal by shining X-rays of known wavelength, (usually about 1 Angstrom) on the crystal and measuring the interference and diffraction pattern which results. Much knowledge of atomic and ionic spacings in crystals is found in this way. Inter-atomic distances are generally 1 or 2 Angstroms in solids.

Infra-red Radiation — has a wave length greater than that of red light, between 7,500 Angstroms and 0.03 centimeters. The energy carried by infra-red waves is often absorbed by molecular substances and used to cause them to rotate and vibrate. Just as the frequency of a pendulum is influenced by its length, the frequency of vibration or rotation of a molecule is influenced by the shape of the molecule. Observing the infra-red frequencies absorbed by a substance gives information about vibrational frequencies and hence of atom-atom bond angles and bond lengths.

UNIT 9

ELECTRON ARRANGEMENT AND THE PERIODIC TABLE

The atom which is most fully understood is the simplest atom — that of hydrogen. Most of what is known about the electron behaviour in hydrogen atoms has been learned by studying the light which these atoms emit after they have become excited by the addition of energy. This added energy excites the atom by moving the electron to a greater distance from the nucleus; the energy is used to overcome the attractive force between the proton and electron.

Just as the gravitational potential energy of a suspended book is partially converted to sound energy when the book falls, the electrical potential energy of an excited atom is totally converted to light energy when the electron "falls" to a level closer to the nucleus. The frequency, ν, of the emitted radiation is directly proportional to the difference in energy between the initial and final states. The proportionality constant, h, is called Planck's constant and has a value, determined experimentally, of 1.5×10^{-34} calorie-sec.

This information is summarized in the equation called Planck's relationship.

$$E = h\nu$$

where E represents the energy of the packet or "photon" of light emitted during the transition.

When a high voltage is applied across a tube of hydrogen gas, light of various colours is produced. When this light is dispersed by a prism to form a spectrum it is found that only a few special wavelengths are ever produced.

Example: One of the "permitted" wavelengths which can be found in the spectrum of hydrogen is in the ultra-violet with $\lambda = 1216$ Angstroms. How much energy must be supplied to one mole of hydrogen atoms to cause them all to undergo the transition which generates this spectral line?

Solution: Working to two significant figures, the wave length will be 1.2×10^3 Angstroms or more practically, 1.2×10^{-5} cm.

$$\text{The frequency} = \nu = \frac{c}{\lambda} = \frac{3.0 \times 10^{10}}{1.2 \times 10^{-5}} \frac{\text{cm/sec}}{\text{cm/wave}}$$

$$\nu = 2.5 \times 10^{15} \text{ waves/sec.}$$

The energy which one atom gives to its one photon during emission is found from the Planck relationship.

$$E = h \nu = 1.5 \times 10^{-34} \times 2.5 \times 10^{15}$$
$$= 3.8 \times 10^{-19} \text{ calories.}$$

The energy which one mole of hydrogen atoms gives to 6×10^{23} photons during emission is:

$$3.8 \times 10^{-19} \frac{\text{calories}}{\text{photon}} \times 6 \times 10^{23} \frac{\text{photons}}{\text{mole}}$$

$$= 23 \times 10^4 \frac{\text{calories}}{\text{mole}} \text{ or approximately}$$

230 kilocalories per mole of emitting atoms. The accepted answer is 235.2 kcal/mole.

A person climbing a ladder will have his feet come to rest at only certain definite heights above the ground. It appears than an electron which is being excited away from the nucleus can move into only certain definite energy states or levels or conditions. To raise electrons from a lower energy state to higher requires the addition of energy in some form; the drop from a higher level to a lower level liberates the energy as radiation.

Calculations similar to the previous example show that a hydrogen line in the ultra-violet with $\lambda = 1026$ Angstroms is caused by changes between energy levels involving 278.8 kcal/mole. A hydrogen line in the red part of the visible spectrum with $\lambda = 6565$ Angstroms is produced by electron transitions involving only 43.6 kcal/mole. (Note that ultra-violet radiation is more energetic and hence potentially more dangerous than visible).

After much detective work, the various lines in the hydrogen spectrum were arranged into several series. Two of these are outlined briefly here.

Lyman Series — a set of lines in the ultra-violet formed when electrons fall to the lowest energy level from higher levels.

Balmer Series — a set of lines in the visible and near ultra-violet formed when electrons fall to the second lowest energy level from higher levels.

For example, an electron excited to the third lowest energy level is going to tend to return to the lowest or ground state, just as a thrown ball tends to return to earth. The excited electron has two ways by which it may return:

(a) it may fall directly from the third lowest level to the lowest: energy change = 278.8 kcal/mole, $\lambda = 1026$ A.

(b) it may "bounce" from the third lowest to the second lowest to the lowest. This change involves two emissions. The first has E = 43.6 kcal/mole, λ = 6565 A. The second has E = 235.2 kcal/mole, λ = 1216 A. Notice that the total energy emitted by the two transitions is the same as that in (a).

Spectroscopy is a branch of physics which is concerned with wave lengths of light and the corresponding energy transitions. Many years work by many persons were required to accumulate the information which helped to make the development of this theory of energy levels possible.

Quantum numbers are integers which identify the various permitted or "stationary" states of an atom. For example, the above account of hydrogen may be quite well summarized in the following equation, found experimentally and also derived theoretically;

$$E_n = 313.6 - \frac{313.6}{n^2}$$

where n is the principal quantum number and E_n is the amount of energy which was absorbed by the atom during its excitation to the nth level.

Explanation: When the atom is in the lowest or ground state,

$$n = 1, E_1 = 313.6 - 313.6 = 0$$

When the atom is in the second lowest state,

$$n = 2, E_2 = 313.6 - \frac{313.6}{4} = 235.2 \text{ kcal/mole.}$$

When the atom is in the third lowest state,

$$n = 3, E_3 = 313.6 - \frac{313.6}{9} = 278.8 \text{ kcal/mole.}$$

These values calculated for the second and third lowest states are in agreement with the measured values used previously.

In general; when an electron drops from level E_2 to level E_1

$$\Delta E = h\nu = E_2 - E_1$$

Orbitals — are representations of the distribution of an electron in space about an atomic nucleus. Orbitals can best be described for the hydrogen atom in which there are no complications arising from electron — electron interactions. The following descriptions apply to hydrogen atoms.

When the atom is in the ground state (n = 1) the electron is likely to be contained in an imaginary sphere (radius roughly 1 Angstrom) about the nucleus. The electron is moving quickly and its distance from the nucleus changes constantly. The average value for the pro-ton—electron distance is about 0.5 Angstroms. This spherical region is called the spherical orbital of the first energy level and is repre-sented by "1s", (Figure 9-1).

In higher energy levels p, d and f orbitals are encountered. The p orbitals are dumbbell shaped (centered about the nucleus) and are always mutually perpendicular or polarized along the x, y, and z axes, (Figure 9-2) The d and f orbitals can not be simply described.

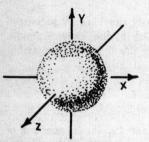

Perspective diagram of 1s orbital

(Fig. 9-1)

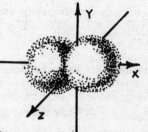

Perspective diagram of a p orbital

(Fig. 9-2)

In the second level (n = 2), there are 4 orbitals: one 2s orbital and three perpendicular 2p orbitals.

In the third level (n = 3), there are 9 orbitals: one 3s orbital and three 3p orbitals and five 3d orbitals.

In the fourth level (n = 4), there are 16 orbitals: one 4s, three 4p, five 4d and seven 4f orbitals. Notice that:

(a) every level has the same type of orbitals as the previous one, plus a different type of orbital.

(b) Any orbital may be described by a number indicating the level and a letter which indicates the type of distribution.

(c) In a given level, the s orbital has lower energy than the p orbi-tals; the p orbitals have less energy than the d orbitals.

(d) The nth level contains n^2 orbitals.

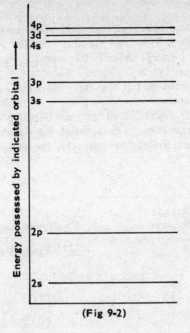

(Fig 9-2)

Many-electron atoms are more complicated because of the presence of more than one moving charge, but the concept of s, p, d and f orbitals seems to apply to them. The idea of electron arrangements about a positive nucleus, discovered by study of the simplest atom, applies to the more complicated atoms.

Modern theories of stellar evolution (i.e. stars are "born", pass through "youth" "middle age" "old age" and "death") indicate that all atoms heavier than hydrogen were synthesized by nuclear fusion in stellar interiors. The way in which these newly formed nuclei arrange their electrons can be imagined with the help of three rules.

(a) The Pauli Principle states that no orbital can hold more than two electrons. The electrons have the same energy.

(b) Orbitals of equivalent energy are filled singly before electron pairing occurs. That is, one would not expect to find a filled 2p orbital in an atom which had an empty 2p orbital.

(c) Orbitals of low energy are filled before orbitals of high energy.

Build-up of the Periodic Table
When a helium nucleus acquires electrons, two electrons fill the 1s orbital to create a stable atom. The configuration is $1s^2$. The superscript indicates the number of electrons occupying the orbital.

When a lithium nucleus (At. No. = 3) acquires electrons, the 1s orbital becomes filled. The third electron required for neutrality goes into the next lowest energy orbital, the s orbital of the second level. The configuration is $1s^2 2s^1$.

The orbitals continue to fill regularly until the atomic number reaches 19, (potassium).

The valence of argon is listed as zero because the atoms of this element, like all noble gas atoms, have their highest occupied energy level completely filled. Accordingly, the atoms have very little tendency to react.

Element	Atomic Number	Configuration	Valence
Oxygen	8	$1s^2 2s^2 2p_x^2 2p_y^1 2p_z^1$ or $1s^2 2s^2 2p^4$	−2
Magnesium	12	$3s^2$	+2
Chlorine	17	$3s^2 3p^5$	−1
Argon	18	$1s^2\ 2s^2\ 2p^6$ $\begin{cases} 3s^2 3p^6 \end{cases}$	0
Potassium	19	$3s^2 3p^6 4s^1$	+1
Calcium	20	$3s^2 3p^6 4s^2$	+2
Scandium	21	$3s^2 3p^6 3d^1 4s^2$	+2

The s orbital of the fourth level has less energy than the d orbital of the third level. For this reason electrons numbered 19 and 20 go into the 4s orbital.

The five d orbitals of the third level have less energy than the p orbitals of the fourth level. This means that electrons numbered between 21 and 30 will be placed in the 3d orbitals.

The result is a series of 10 elements which have two electrons in the outer, 4s, orbital and increasing numbers of electrons in the 3d orbitals. A common oxidation number for this series of elements is +2, but other values are possible because some of the electrons in the 3d orbitals are available for reaction with a substance which has a great affinity for electrons. The elements chromium and manganese which show oxidation numbers of +6 and +7 in the ions CrO_4^{-2} and MnO_4^- respectively belong to this "transition series."

The progressive filling of the inner levels of these atoms, whose outer levels contain only a few electrons, explains why there are many more metallic elements than non-metallic elements.

Ionization Energy and Electron Arrangement

The ionization energy of an element is the amount of work which must be done to pull the most loosely held electron to an infinite separation from the nucleus.

Looking across the periodic table from an alkali metal such as lithium (At. No. = 3) to the inert gas in the same row, neon (At. No. = 10) the ionization energy rises, indicating a decreasing tendency to form positive ions.

Looking down the periodic table we also find a decrease in ionization energies. The heavy alkali metals loose electrons more readily, partially because the electron clouds of the large atoms tend to screen the nuclear charge.

The second ionization energy is the amount of work which must be done to remove the most loosely held electron from a singly charged positive ion. The value must be greater than the first ionization energy for that element because the ion exerts a greater attractive force on its electrons than the atom did.

Sodium looses its 3s electron readily but to further ionize Na^+ requires the removal of a 2p electron which is firmly held. The second ionization energy for sodium is high.

Aluminum looses its 3p electron and then its two 3s electrons fairly readily. The removal of electrons from the 2p orbitals requires much energy.

The number of "valence electrons" in an atom is the number of electrons which must be lost before the partially occupied level is emptied. (This does not apply to the transition series elements). For example, aluminum ($1s^2 2s^2 2p^6 3s^2 3p^1$) has three valence electrons; fluorine ($1s^2 2s^2 2p^5$) has seven valence electrons.

UNIT 10

MOLECULES IN THE GAS PHASE

A covalent bond is the linkage which holds different atoms together in a molecule. The element with the simplest atoms, hydrogen,
also forms the simplest diatomic molecule. This is not a coincidence:
the atom is the simplest because it has only two particles — the
diatomic molecule formed will then have only four particles.

When two atoms approach in an attempt to form a molecule there
will always be repulsive forces (proton-proton and electron-electron)
and attractive forces (proton-electron). If the attractive forces are
sufficiently strong to overcome the repulsive forces, then a covalent
or molecular bond will result.

When two hydrogen atoms unite to form a molecule they approach
so that their 1s orbitals overlap. The electrons can move anywhere
within the orbitals, but they tend to remain between the two nuclei,
acting as a type of "electrical cement" which holds the protons together. The electrons are attracted to, and hence attract, the two
nuclei.

Another way to understand the bonding is this: when the orbitals
are overlapped there is a probability that each atom will have its
1s orbital filled at least part of the time. The more closely the electron configuration approaches that of helium, the more stable (less
reactive) the structure becomes.

A covalent bond is formed when each of the bonded or linked atoms
has contributed an electron to the shared orbital region.

Helium gas does not form diatomic molecules, indicating that the
repulsive forces (nucleus-nucleus, electron-electron) are stronger
than the attractive forces (nucleus-electron). This is consistent with
the concept that helium already has an electron configuration $1s^2$.
The filled 1s shells would have little tendency to overlap.

Representation of Chemical Bonding

This may be done in two ways. The longer, which conveys more
information, involves the representation of each orbital by a circle.
The number of electrons present in the orbital (none, one or two) is
represented by an equal number of lines. Atoms which have a partially filled set of orbitals tend to react.

Example: By orbital representation show the bonding which occurs
in molecular fluorine (At. No. = 9).

Solution: The spacings of the circles which represent the orbitals
should be roughly proportional to the orbital energy.

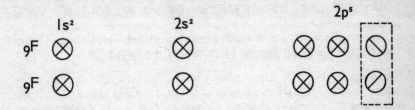

The overlapping of two 2p orbitals leads to the bonding in molecular fluorine.

The shorter method of showing bonding involves representing the the valence electrons by dots and the rest of the atom by the symbol for that element.

Example: By electron dot diagrams show the reaction between two fluorine atoms (At. No. = 9).

$$\overset{..}{\underset{..}{:F\cdot}} \;\; + \;\; \overset{\times\times}{\underset{\times\times}{{}^{\times}F_{\times}}} \longrightarrow \overset{..}{\underset{..}{:F_{\times}}}\overset{\times\times}{\underset{\times\times}{F_{\times}}}$$

The small crosses and dots are used, not to indicate any basic difference between electrons but to emphasize that each atom contributes one electron to the bond. This type of representation makes it easy to see that the energy level of each atom has been filled — cover first one side of the product and then the other.

The element considered in this example is the most reactive nonmetal. Fluorine atoms have a great attracting power, or affinity, for electrons. The charge of the 9 protons is lightly screened by electrons and there is a great tendency to acquire the one electron needed to completely fill the highest occupied energy level.

The atoms of the progressively lighter elements in the second row of the periodic table show progressively less tendency to acquire electrons i.e. lower electron affinities.

Bonding of Elements of the Second Row — Lithium to Oxygen —

Oxygen atoms (At. No. = 8) have 6 valence electrons and each must acquire two electrons to complete the second energy level. Reactive metals combine with oxygen to form ionic oxides, but many of the compounds of oxygen are molecular. The orbital representation is:

$$_8O \quad \overset{1s^2}{\otimes} \qquad\qquad \overset{2s^2}{\otimes} \qquad\qquad\qquad \overset{2p^4}{\otimes\;\oslash\;\oslash}$$

Note that the 2p orbitals each receive one electron before any receive a second.

Water molecules are formed when 1s orbitals of hydrogen atoms overlap the dumbbell shaped p orbitals of the oxygen.

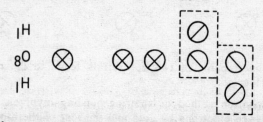

The electron dot representation of the water molecule is

Nitrogen atoms (At. No. = 7) have a weaker nuclear charge and require three electrons to complete the second energy level. Only reactions with the more active metals form the nitride ion N^{-3}: usually the nitrogen atom employs covalent bonds. The electron configuration is:

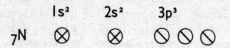

The compound formed with hydrogen is ammonia, which contains the expected 3 atoms of hydrogen per molecule.

$$
\begin{array}{ccc}
\text{H} & \overset{..}{\underset{\times}{\text{N}}} \overset{}{} & \text{H} \\
 & \overset{\times\,\cdot}{\text{H}} &
\end{array}
$$

Carbon atoms (At. No. = 6) continue the trend to lower electron affinity. One electron configuration is:

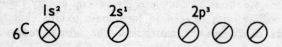

One 2s electron is frequently "promoted" to the 2p level, an event which results in a high degree of symetry in compounds such as methane, CH₄.

$$\begin{array}{c} \overset{\cdot x}{H} \\ H\overset{x}{\cdot}\;\;C\;\;\overset{x}{\cdot}H \\ \overset{\cdot x}{H} \end{array}$$

This results from a process of "hybridization": the three singly occupied 2p orbitals and the one singly occupied 2s orbital, re-arrange to form four identical orbitals which are called s-p-three or sp³ orbitals. The superscript indicates the number of p orbitals which were used in the mixing.

Boron atoms (At. No. = 5) do not tend to form ions. The compounds are generally molecular, formed by the bonding which results after one 2s electron is promoted to a 2p orbital. A common electron configuration for boron:

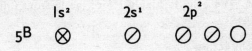

The one singly occupied 2s orbital and the two singly occupied 2p orbitals again "hybridize" to form three identical sp² orbitals.

These three sp² orbitals are used in the bonding which results in the formation of very reactive boron trihydride, BH_3. The unfilled 2p orbitals are likely used in the formation of compounds such as diborane, B_2H_6.

Beryllium atoms (At. No. = 4) do not readily loose two electrons to form ions. Generally one 2s electron is promoted to a 2p orbital. Hybridization of the two results in the formation of two sp orbitals. These are used in the bonding of compounds such as beryllium dihydride, BeH_2. The two unoccupied 2p orbitals are used in the bonding which holds the molecules in a high melting point solid.

Lithium atoms (At. No. = 3) are able to yield their single 2s electrons to form a univalent positive ion. The electron configuration of the atom:

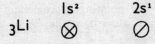

The range of electron affinity encountered in the second row of the table is also illustrated by the type of bond the different elements use when they are bonded to fluorine.

In molecular fluorine, the electron pair is equally shared between the identical atoms. In difluorine oxide, F_2O, the electron pairs are shifted somewhat toward the fluorine atom. In the extreme case of lithium fluoride, LiF, there is no "shared pair" — the 2s orbital of lithium is emptied and the second energy level of fluorine is filled. The bonding is ionic rather than molecular or covalent:

$$\overset{+}{Li} \quad {}_{x} \overset{..}{\overset{-}{F}}:$$

The "shared pair" is almost entirely in the fluorine orbital.

In a similar fashion, the hydrogen compounds of second row elements show the changing electron affinites. A carbon-hydrogen bond is highly covalent: the electron pair is moving freely between the atoms. A fluorine-hydrogen bond has the electron pair shifted toward the fluorine atom. The fluorine atom is thus slightly negative, the hydrogen atom is slightly positive. At the lighter end of the row we find that the electron pair in lithium hydride is attracted towards the hydrogen atom. The bond is highly ionic: the hydrogen atom is negative in this case.

Molecular Architecture

The shapes of the molecules of the compounds formed by the second row elements are easily understood and remembered when the type of orbitals used in the bonding are known. Some typical examples are outlined below.

(1) When oxygen reacts with hydrogen or fluorine, the oxygen atom uses its two partially filled, perpendicular 2p orbitals. In water, the angle between the two hydrogen-oxygen bonds opens to 104.5°; in difluorine oxide, F_2O, the angle between the two fluorine-oxygen bonds is 102°. Both molecules are planar or flat because they are triatomic.

(2) When nitrogen reacts with hydrogen or fluorine, the nitrogen atom uses its three partially full 2p orbitals. The resulting molecules are ammonia NH_3 and nitrogen trifluoride, NF_3. If you adjust your thumb, index finger and middle finger so that they represent the mutually perpendicular 2p orbitals of a nitrogen atom, then your hand is representing the nitrogen atom and your three digits are pointing approximately toward the bonded atoms. The nitrogen atom is at the top of a triangular pyramid. The H-N-H bond angle is 107°.

Some authorities believe that the nitrogen atom in the ammonia molecule uses sp^3 hybridization: the two 2s electrons and the three 2p electrons would be distributed so that three of the sp^3 orbitals are singly filled and the fourth is completely filled. The completely filled sp³ orbital can then be used to explain the existence of the ammonium ion, NH_4^+, and of other ions which ammonia can form with electron deficient ions as is illustrated by Experiment (c) of Unit 14.

(3) When carbon reacts with hydrogen or fluorine to form methane, CH_4, or carbon tetrafluoride, CF_4, the carbon atom employs four equivalent sp³ orbitals which are separated by an angle of 109.5°. The resulting molecule has the carbon atom centrally situated in a triangular pyramid or tetrahedron. In the methane tetrahedron, any three of the hydrogen atoms form an equilateral triangle and the fourth hydrogen atom is centered above (or below) the triangle; the carbon atom is 1.09 Angstroms away from each of the hydrogen atoms.

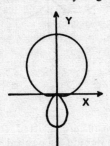

(Fig. 10-1)

Cross section of a sp³ hybrid orbital

(4) When boron uses sp² orbitals the molecules are planar with bond angles of 120°. This is because the three sp² orbitals are in the same plane (i.e. lie on the same surface) and are equally spaced with an angle of 120° between each, (Figure 10-2).

(Fig. 10-2)

Cross section of a sp² hybrid orbital

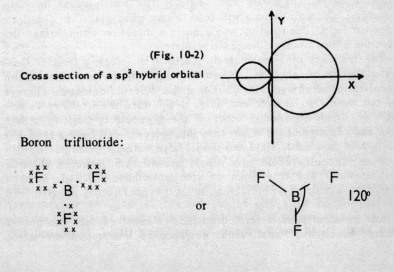

Boron trifluoride:

or

In the second diagram above the unshared valence electrons are not shown. Each shared pair of electrons is represented by a single line.

(5) Beryllium difluoride is formed when beryllium uses two equivalent sp orbitals. The molecule is linear because the angle between the two sp orbitals 180°. (Figure 10-3).

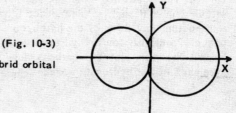

(Fig. 10-3)

Cross section of a sp hybrid orbital

Beryllium difluoride

$$\overset{\times\times}{\underset{\times\times}{\times}}\overset{}{F}\overset{\times}{\cdot} \quad Be \quad \overset{\times\times}{\cdot}\overset{}{F}\overset{\times}{\underset{\times\times}{\times}} \quad \text{or} \quad F - Be - F$$

In the BeF_2 molecule the electron pairs are shifted toward the fluorine atoms. The result is that the molecule is neutral but has a positive center and negative ends. If this molecule were placed between two equally and oppositely charge plates, then it would have no tendency to turn. This is because both ends of this "stick" molecule are equally negative — neither end is attracted preferentially be the positive plate.

In the F_2O molecule the electron pairs are shifted toward the fluorine atoms. The F-O-F bond angle is 102° which means that this roughly L shaped molecule will tend to turn when placed in a uniform electric field. The rotation would be in a direction which brings the fluorine atoms towards the positive plate.

The tendency of a molecule to rotate in an electric field is indicated by the molecule's "dipole moment". If the molecule has no localization of charge (e.g. CH_4) or if the molecule has equal charges of the same sign at each end, (e.g. BeF_2), then the tendency to turn and the dipole moment is zero. If the molecule is positive at one end and negative at the other, then the molecule will have a tendency to turn in an electric field and it will have a dipole moment.

Some molecules which have dipole moments are: hydrogen chloride (HCl), water and chloroform or trichloromethane ($CHCl_3$). In each case the active non-metal (chlorine or oxygen) is the negative end or pole of the molecule.

Any covalent bond described so far has involved only one pair of shared electrons. Experimental evidence indicates that the atoms of oxygen in hydrogen peroxide H-O-O-H are further apart than the atoms of oxygen in molecular oxygen O_2. This indicates that the forces holding the oxygen atoms together in O_2 are stronger and are caused by two pairs of shared electrons. The two pairs of electrons shared between two atoms constitute a double bond.

Similarly, the distance between carbon atoms in ethane, C_2H_6, is greater than the distance between carbon atoms in ethylene C_2H_4. In ethylene a double bond draws the carbon atoms closer together.

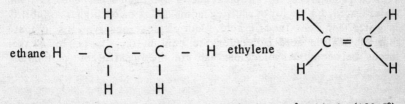

In the ethane bonding carbon uses equivalent sp^3 orbitals (109.5°). In ethylene, each carbon atom uses three sp^2 orbitals lying in a plane. A single, partially filled p orbital of each carbon atom extends above and below the plane. The second bond is a relatively weak one formed by the partial overlap of the two paralled p orbitals, (Figure 10-4).

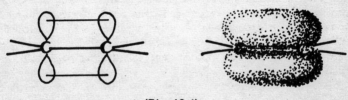

(Fig. 10-4)

Because carbon-carbon double bonds are formed in this way the two carbon atoms can not rotate with respect to each other as they do in ethane. Such a rotation in ethylene would cause the already weakly overlapped p orbitals of the second bond to move apart. This is not likely to happen.

The lack of rotation of the carbon-carbon double bond results in the existence of pairs of "cis-trans isomers". For example:

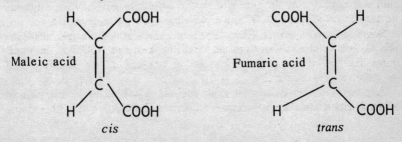

Explanation: Isomers have the same molecular formula, in this case $C_4H_4O_4$.

The *trans* isomer has the COOH or "carboxylic acid" groups on opposite sides of the double bond. This is shown by fumaric acid.

The *cis* isomer has the COOH groups on the same side of the double bond. This is shown by maleic acid.

Because rotation about the double bond occurs only with difficulty, maleic acid has little tendency to turn into fumaric acid. The conversion is catalyzed by the presence of hydrogen ions. The *cis* form, maleic acid, has a lower melting point and a much higher solubility in water than does fumaric acid. Both of these observations indicate that the maleic acid molecules are held in the crystal by weaker forces between the molecules than are the fumaric acid molecules.

UNIT 11

THE BONDING IN SOLIDS AND LIQUIDS

Elements

Gaseous elements such as neon, Ne, or fluorine, F_2, have all the valence orbitals filled and are uniformly neutral. Hence there is very little tendency for the individual molecules to attract each other into a solid or liquid state. However, forces do exist between the nuclei in one molecule and the electrons in other molecules. At low temperatures the molecules are moving relatively slowly and these weak forces are able to hold the molecules together in a condensed state of matter. These weak electrical forces which act between molecules are called van der Waals forces. The elements which behave as van der Waals liquids and solids are generally those at the top right of the periodic table: fluorine, oxygen, nitrogen and others.

Some solid elements are held together in network solids by covalent bonds linking the identical atoms together in a great three dimensional array. Diamonds are formed when carbon atoms become bonded together using sp^3 orbitals. Each carbon atom is linked by strong bonds to four other carbon atoms; each one of these four atoms is joined to four atoms. A great deal of energy is required to pull atoms out of such a structure.

A softer and more common form of pure carbon is graphite. Graphite is composed of planar sheets of carbon atoms, in which each atom is linked to three others using sp^2 orbitals. The third, unhybridized p orbital of each carbon atom extends above and below the plane, as it does in ethylene. The partial overlap of these p orbitals holds the sheets of carbon atoms in place but does permit some slippage.

On the periodic table, the elements which form network solids are generally found to the left of elements forming molecular solids and to the right of metallic elements. Examples — carbon, silicon, arsenic and bismuth.

Metallic elements are usually recognized by their silvery lustre. This results from the total reflection of all frequencies of visible light. This silvery lustre may be readily observed when an object is first "sooted" by placing it in a candle flame and is then lowered into water. (The sooty object becomes surrounded with air when placed in water and becomes a total reflector). This implies that there is something quite unusual about the electron distribution in metals because light emission and absorption (or lack of it) depends very strongly upon the electron energies of the atoms involved.

The tendency of metals to be good conductors of electricity suggests that charged particles, most likely electrons, are free to move through the solid. The high thermal conductivity can be explained in terms of high kinetic energy electrons drifting away from a hot region toward a cooler region. The high tendency of metallic elements, which are found on the left side of the table, to form positive ions points to the existence of easily removed electrons.

The ease with which metals may be hammered into sheets or drawn into fine wires indicates that attractive forces act between the atoms but that there is no strong tendency for these forces to be oriented in a particular direction. Thus, a metal bowl becomes dented rather than cracked or shattered when it is dropped.

The theory or "model" which emerges for a typical metal such as magnesium is this: the atoms are packed together with their almost empty valence orbitals overlapped. The extensive overlap of many orbitals gives the relatively few valence electrons a large region in which they may freely move. The sea of electrons whizzing about in the solid between positive centers holds the assemblage together. The result of the fluid electrons is the metallic, non-directed bond.

Any valence electron at any time is attracted to several nuclei. Just as the magnet which attracts a nail is attracted to the nail, the nuclei which attract a valence electron are all attracted toward the valence electron. The resulting bond is weaker than covalent bonds: the quantity of energy required to vaporize one mole of an alkali metal is about one quarter of that required to break one mole of covalent bonds. This is to be expected: if the atom has little tendency to attract its own valence electrons, then it will have little tendency to attract its neighbour's. The electrons are left to move in a region of uniformly low potential energy.

Compounds

The two or more different types of atoms which one finds in a compound are also held together by electrical forces.

Molecular compounds which are polar tend to have strong forces holding the molecules in the liquid or solid. These forces arise from positive-negative attraction between the ends of different molecules. Example: water, hydrogen chloride.

Molecular compounds which are non-polar have no strong forces between their molecules and tend to form van der Waals liquids and solids. Example: carbon dioxide, methane.

The magnitude of the van der Waals force is determined to a large extent by the surface area of the molecules. Ethane, C_2H_6, and hexane, C_6H_{14}, are both substances which have non-polar molecules, yet the former is a gas, the latter is a liquid at room conditions. This is caused mainly by the greater surface area of the larger molecule which increases the chance of interaction with neighbours. This results in an increase in the size of molecule-molecule forces. In order of increasing surface area and of increasing boiling point, some van der Waals elements are: F_2, Cl_2, Br_2, I_2; some van der Waals compounds are: CF_4, CCl_4, CBr_4, CI_4.

The molecular weight in the above examples is also increasing but this has little effect on the changing properties. For example, maleic and fumaric acids have identical molecular weights, yet the former melts at 130⁰C, the latter at 387⁰C. The difference in this case is caused by the difference in the shape of the *cis* and *trans* isomers.

Compounds may also occur as network solids. The most familiar examples of this type of covalent bonding are found in the various compounds of oxygen and silicon.

In each one of the following three examples an oxygen atom serves to unite two silicon atoms. The basic repeated pattern is that of a silicon atom linked to another silicon atom by means of an oxygen atom:

$$-Si-O-Si-$$

Asbestos minerals are formed from long chains of atoms in which each silicon atom is bonded to two oxygen atoms and each oxygen atom is bonded to two silicon atoms. The other two partially filled orbitals of each silicon atom are used in bonding to atoms of other elements. The mineral is fibrous, (Figure 11-1).

Mica minerals are formed from sheets of atoms in which each silicon atom is joined to three oxygen atoms and each oxygen atom is joined to two silicon atoms. The fourth partially filled orbital of each silicon atom is bonded to an atom of another element. The mineral is composed of many thin sheets, (Figure 11-2).

Quartz is a hard substance with a high melting point. Each atom of silicon is bonded to four oxygen atoms. Each oxygen atom is bonded to two silicon atoms. The growing crystal tends to spread equally in three dimensions, giving beautiful crystals. Amethyst is a form of nearly pure quartz. (Figure 11-3).

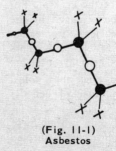

(Fig. 11-1)
Asbestos

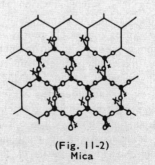

(Fig. 11-2)
Mica

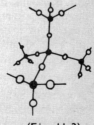

(Fig. 11-3)
Quartz

● Silicon   O Oxygen   X Other atoms

Alloys are solid solutions containing two or more types of atoms, usually metallic, dispersed uniformly throughout the crystal. Each atom uses its normal non-directed metallic bond in its linkage with its neighbours, which may or may not be the same kind of atom. The composition of an alloy such as brass can vary widely, hence the substance is a solution rather than a compound.

When a trace of impurity is added to a metallic element, the resulting solid is often found to have decreased metallic characteristics. For example, the addition of silicon to copper introduces directed bonds which interfere with electron flow and flexibility.

Ionic solids are compounds which are formed when one of the reacting atoms has a sufficiently high attraction for electrons to empty the valence orbitals of the other. The captured electrons are not mobile but are confined to the orbitals of the negative ions. The positive and negative ions arrange themselves into orderly arrays so that the nearest neighbours of any ion have a charge opposite to that of the ion. The result is a well defined crystal in which each one of millions of ions is suspended in the strong electric fields of its neighbours. Such substances have a high melting point, low electrical conductivity while solid and high electrical conductivity when molten.

An ionic solid such as sodium chloride, NaCl, has very strong forces holding the ions together. The solid has little tendency to dissolve in carbon tetrachloride and must be heated above 800°C before the ions acquire enough energy to permit separation. Yet this separation may be done at room temperature using water as a solvent. Each dissolving ion gets surrounded by water molecules which become bound to the ion so that the negative ends of the water molecules (oxygen atoms) are near the cations (sodium ions), and the positive ends of the water molecules (hydrogen atoms) are near the anions. This partial restriction or "tying up" of water molecules results in a release of energy similar to that found when water freezes.

Usually, dissolving is a process which absorbs heat as work is done removing particles from the attractive forces of the crystal. But when the solvent is water, so much energy may be released by the aquation or hydration process that the temperature rises. For example, care should be taken when dissolving relatively large amounts of sodium hydroxide in water because of the high heat of solution.

Many compounds exist as molecules which are somewhat polar. Such compounds have melting points greater than those of van der Waals solids and less than those of ionic solids.

Polar molecules tend to dissolve well in solvents which have polar molecules; the positive parts of the solute are attracted to and likely to form a union with the negative parts of the solvent molecules. Similarly, a non-polar solvent, (such as carbon tetra-chloride), has less difficulty accepting a non-polar solute, (such as ethane C_2H_6), than does a polar solvent.

Hydrogen bonding occurs when a hydrogen atom which is bonded by a rather polar bond to an atom of an active non-metal becomes loosely bonded to a second atom of an active non-metal. The second atom may be in the same or a different molecule.

Examples of hydrogen bonding

(1) Water molecules are quite small and have a small surface area, yet the melting point and boiling point are high. This is attributed to hydrogen bonding between the different molecules. Each O-H bond is quite polar: the electron pair is shifted toward the oxygen atom. Thus the slightly positive hydrogen atom of one molecule may be attracted to the negative oxygen atom of another water molecule.

$$H^+ \quad {}^-O - H^+ \ldots {}^-O \underset{H^+}{\overset{H^+}{\diagdown}}$$

The increased attractive forces hold the molecules more strongly in the solid or liquid. The formation of a mole of hydrogen bonds releases from 3 to 7 kilocalories.

(2) Hydrogen bonding can occur within one molecule. The low melting point of maleic acid relative to fumaric acid is explained in terms of hydrogen bonding. The formula for maleic acid is:

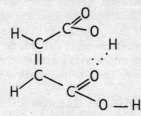

The *cis* form places the slightly positive hydrogen atom of the OH group close to the slightly negative oxygen atom of the C = O group. The result: an internal or intramolecular bond and one less hydrogen atom which is available to bond the molecule to its neighbours. The *trans* form has the two COOH groups diametrically opposed with no opportunity for internal hydrogen bonding. Both hydroxyl hydrogen atoms are then used for intermolecular bonding.

Hydrogen bonding is also encountered in compounds such as hydrogen fluoride, HF, and ammonia, NH_3. In each case, the effect of the intermolecular bonding is to raise the melting and boiling points above those which would be expected for such small area molecules.

UNIT 12

THE CHEMISTRY OF CARBON COMPOUNDS

The gas carbon dioxide occupies about 0.03% by volume of the earth's atmosphere. This low concentration, about 3 litres in 10,000, is sufficient to support the process of photosynthesis by which more complicated molecules containing carbon are produced in plants. These organic molecules have various possible futures. Some become oxidized to release carbon dioxide and water and energy to support the life of plants. Some become eaten by animals and are used to supply energy to the animals, or, after some rearrangement, are incorporated into the cells of the animals. If the organisms containing the organic molecules become buried under pressure with no possibility of oxidation, then coal or petroleum deposits will result.

Coal is a solid which is rich in carbon with varying amounts of oxygen, hydrogen, nitrogen and sulphur. Coal is formed by the covering and compacting of forests over a long period of time. When heated in the absence of air (to prevent oxidation) coal produces a mixture of low molecular weight gases, (coal gas), a liquid solution (coal tar) and a solid very rich in carbon (coke).

Petroleum is a liquid which is a complex solution of various hydrogen-carbon (or hydrocarbon) compounds. The other elements which are found in coal are usually found in petroleum also. Petroleum deposits are usually associated with buried oceanic life. Natural gas is a solution of low molecular weight gases such as methane, CH_4, and ethane, C_2H_6, which is frequently found with petroleum deposits. The pressure exerted by the gas may be used to force the petroleum to the surface if the well is properly drilled. In some cases, the natural gas has been piped off, leaving great deposits of buried petroleum with no agent to force them to the surface.

MOLECULAR STRUCTURES OF CARBON COMPOUNDS

There are many hundreds of thousands of carbon compounds. The key to an understanding of the behaviour of any particular compound is the knowledge of the structure of the molecules of that substance. This includes a knowledge of the kind, number and arrangement of atoms in the molecule.

Identification of the elements present is usually done by converting a sample of the compound to simpler substances. All organic compounds produce carbon dioxide and water when burned. If the compound is thought to contain nitrogen or sulphur, then a sample of the compound should be treated with molten sodium and the products analyzed for the presence of sodium cyanide, NaCN, or sodium sulphide, Na_2S.

The empirical formula for a compound shows the kind and relative number of atoms in its molecules.

Example: The combustion of 2.6 gm of acetylene, a hydrocarbon, produces 8.8 gm of carbon dioxide and 1.8 gm of water. Calculate the empirical formula of acetylene.

Solution: Carbon dioxide is 12/44 carbon by weight.

$$\therefore \ 8.8 \text{ gm of carbon dioxide has } \frac{12}{44} \times 8.8 = 2.4 \text{ gm. carbon.}$$

Water is 2/18 or 1/9 hydrogen by weight.

$$\therefore \ 1.8 \text{ gm of water has } \frac{1}{9} \times 1.8 = 0.2 \text{ gm. hydrogen.}$$

The acetylene sample contained 2.4 gm (0.2 moles) of carbon and 0.2 gm (0.2 moles) of hydrogen. In this case, the number of atoms of hydrogen equals the number of atoms of carbon in the sample; the simplest formula which shows this is CH. The empirical formula for acetylene is CH.

The molecular formula shows the kind and actual number of atoms in a molecule of the substance. It is obtained from two experimentally determined quantities: empirical formula and molecular weight.

Example: Combustion experiments indicate that ethane gas contains three moles of hydrogen for every one mole of carbon. The mass of a volume of ethane is 15/16 the mass of an equal volume of oxygen at the same temperature and pressure.

Find: (a) the empirical formula
(b) the molecular weight
(c) the molecular formula.

Solution:

(a) Because there are three hydrogen atoms for each carbon atom, the empirical formula is CH_3.

(b) The weight of one mole of ethane gas is 15/16 the weight of one mole of oxygen gas. The molecular weight of ethane is $15/16 \times 32 = 30$. One mole of ethane weighs 30 gm.

(c) One mole of CH_3 would weigh 15 gm. This unit must be taken twice to yield a species with a molecular weight of 30. The molecular formula for ethane is $(CH_3)_2$ or more usually C_2H_6.

The final step in the elucidation of the structure is the determination of the arrangement of the atoms within the molecule. This generally involves some detective work and ingenuity; the result is the structural formula for the substance.

Example: Two colourless liquid compounds, A and B, are found to have the molecular formula C_2H_6O.

Liquid A reacts more readily with clean sodium, yielding one mole of hydrogen atoms per mole of C_2H_6O reacted. Liquid A has a higher boiling point than liquid B and is water soluble. What is the probable formula for liquid A?

Solution: The hydrogen atoms are univalent. A hydrogen atom can only be bonded to one other atom and is therefore at the end of any chain.

The oxygen atom is divalent. If both the bonding orbitals are used with hydrogen, water results and no orbitals are available for bonding with carbon. Thus, the oxygen atom must be bonded to one or two carbon atoms.

The carbon atom has four bonding orbitals.

The two possible formulas:

$$\begin{array}{ccccccc}
H & & H & & H & & H \\
| & & | & & | & & | \\
H-C & - & C-O-H & \text{or} & H-C & - O - & C-H \\
| & & | & & | & & | \\
H & & H & & H & & H
\end{array}$$

In each case, all bonding orbitals are filled.

The formula on the left has one hydrogen atom which has definitely different bonding than the other five hydrogen atoms. The hydrogen-oxygen bond bond has more ionic nature than a carbon-hydrogen bond and is more likely to release hydrogen. The relatively loosely held hydrogen atom of the left hand formula, along with the possibility of intermolecular hydrogen bonding by the OH group, indicates that liquid A is represented. The right hand formula represents the less reactive liquid B. Liquid A is ethyl alcohol; liquid B is dimethyl ether.

Structural isomers are compounds with the same molecular formula but different structural formulas. The chemical properties are often quite different. The *cis-trans* isomers, such as maleic and fumaric acids, have structural formulas and chemical properties which are similar: both maleic acid and fumaric acid are acids, one mole of either capable of neutralizing two moles of sodium hydroxide.

SOME CHEMISTRY OF ORGANIC COMPOUNDS

Reactions between organic compounds are often quite slow, requiring in some cases days or weeks to produce a significant quantity of product. This is because the atoms of the reactants are usually firmly bonded and the activation energy is accordingly high: much energy must be localized to permit the required bending or breaking of these bonds.

For example, when methyl bromide is mixed with aqueous sodium hydroxide, the reaction is between the molecule and the hydroxide ion:

$$CH_3Br + OH^- \longrightarrow CH_3OH + Br^-$$

The rate of reaction is increased by increasing the temperature and by increasing the concentration of the hydroxide ion.

The proposed mechanism is this: a molecule of CH_3Br is situated with the bromine atom, say, north of the carbon atom. Then the reacting OH^- ion must be a high energy one approaching the carbon atom from the south. As the negative ion approaches, the three carbon-hydrogen bonds tend to be shifted northward toward the bromine atom. The activated complex is an awkward looking arrangement with three badly strained and distorted C-H bonds and with tentative bonds between the carbon atom and the bromine atom and between the carbon and the hydroxyl group. This unstable complex exists only momentarily: it must decompose with the ejection of either a bromide ion or a hydroxyl ion.

Oxidation of Organic Compounds — Complete oxidation of hydrocarbons produces carbon dioxide and water. Incomplete or partial oxidation of hydrocarbons yields other families of organic compounds.

The alcohol family contains the hydroxyl group, OH, bonded to carbon. The C-OH bond is strong with little tendency to break: if ionization does occur, then hydrogen ions are formed.

Methyl alcohol, CH_3OH, may be considered an oxidation product of methane CH_4; ethyl alcohol, C_2H_5OH, may be considered an oxidation product of ethane C_2H_6.

The aldehyde family, formed by oxidizing alcohols, contains the group:

$$-C \overset{\displaystyle =O}{\underset{\displaystyle \diagdown H}{}}$$

The aldehyde has two less hydrogen atoms than the corresponding alcohol. For example, the oxidation of ethyl alcohol produces acetaldehyde, CH_3CHO.

$$C_2H_5OH \text{ yields } CH_3CHO$$
or

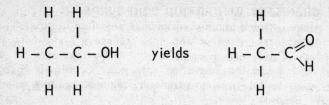

The dichromate ion, $Cr_2O_7^{-2}$, is a suitable oxidizing agent.

The carboxylic acid family is obtained by the oxidation of alde-hydes. In the oxidation, no hydrogen atoms are removed, but an oxy-gen atom is inserted between the carbon and the hydrogen atom of the aldehyde group. For example, the oxidation of acetaldehyde, CH_3CHO, yields acetic acid, CH_3COOH.

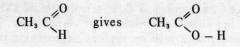

The COOH group is characteristic of most organic acids and is called the carboxylic acid group. When ionization occurs, the hydro-gen ion is released, leaving the carbon atom equally bonded to the two oxygen atoms. The acetate ion is:

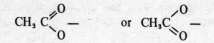

The carbon atom is in effect joined by one and a half bonds to each oxygen atom and the negative charge is shared over a larger area.

Example: Show the successive oxidation products when propanol, $CH_3CH_2CH_2OH$, is oxidized with dichromate or permanganate ions.

Solution:

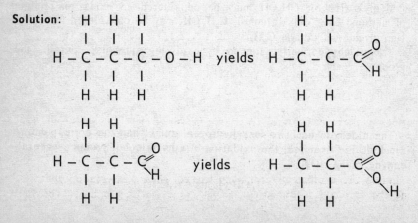

The above mentioned groups OH, CHO and COOH are called functional groups. A functional group is that part of an organic molecule which tends to react. Some molecules have two or more functional groups, others have one or none.

Explanation: Hydrocarbons which have no double or triple bonds are very unreactive and are called alkanes. Generally, each carbon atom in the middle of an alkane chain is bonded to two hydrogen atoms and to two other carbon atoms. Each carbon atom at the end of the chain will be joined to three hydrogen atoms. If there are n carbon atoms in the molecule, then there will be 2n + 2 hydrogen atoms in the molecule. The simplest alkanes are methane, CH_4, and ethane, C_2H_6, in which n = 1 and n = 2 respectively. Other alkanes are propane, C_3H_8; butane, C_4H_{10}; pentane, C_5H_{12} and hexane, C_6H_{14}.

Methyl alcohol, CH_3OH, and ethyl alcohol, CH_3CH_2OH, both possess the OH functional group and therefore exhibit hydrogen bonding and reactivity with sodium metal. The length of the alkane derived, or alkyl, chain bonded to the OH group determines physical properties, such as melting point, rather than the chemical properties of the alcohol.

Frequently, the alkyl groups such as methyl, CH_3; ethyl, C_2H_5; propyl, C_3H_7 and others are represented by the general symbol R. The alkyl groups are never obtained in a pure form — they must always be found with hydrogen or some functional group.

Thus, the general formula for alcohols is ROH, that for aldehydes RCHO and that for carboxylic acids RCOOH.

Ketones are organic compounds in which the functional group, the carboxyl or C = O group, is bonded to two alkyl groups. Each alkyl group is named. Thus, methyl ethyl ketone is:

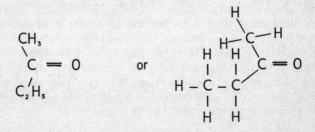

Amines are ammonia derivatives in which one (or more) of the hydrogen atoms has been replaced by an alkyl group. The alkyl group is identified in the name of the amine. Methylamine is CH_3NH_2; dimethylamine is $(CH_3)_2NH$.

Esters are a class of compound formed when a substance containing the carboxylic acid group, COOH, reacts with alcohols. The OH of the acid reacts with the OH of the alcohol, forming a water molecule and leaving one oxygen atom to link the two residues together.

acetic acid + methyl alcohol $\rightleftharpoons$ methyl acetate + water

$$CH_3C\begin{matrix}O\\\\O-H\end{matrix} + CH_3OH \rightleftharpoons CH_3C\begin{matrix}O\\\\O-CH_3\end{matrix} + H_2O$$

The alcohol derived part is named first.

Example: Write the equation for the reaction between ethyl alcohol and propionic acid, CH_3CH_2COOH.

Solution:

Propionic acid + ethyl alcohol $\rightleftharpoons$ ethyl propionate + water.

$$CH_3CH_2C\begin{matrix}O\\\\OH\end{matrix} + CH_3CH_2OH \rightleftharpoons CH_3CH_2C\begin{matrix}O\\\\O-CH_2-CH_3\end{matrix} + H_2O$$

An amide is the compound formed when ammonia reacts with the hydroxyl group of a carboxylic acid. The OH of the acid combines with one hydrogen atom of the ammonia molecule. The acid residue is named first.

For example, acetamide is derived from acetic acid:

$$CH_3C\begin{matrix}O\\\\OH\end{matrix} \quad yields \quad CH_3C\begin{matrix}O\\\\NH_2\end{matrix}$$

In summary, the study of organic chemistry is to a large extent the study of: alcohols, ROH; aldehydes, RCHO; acids, RCOOH; ketones, R_1R_2CO; amines, RNH_2; esters, R_1COOR_2 and amides, $RCONH_2$. In a brief introductory section to organic chemistry it is not possible, nor is it necessary, to discuss the chemistry of all these groups. The purpose of introducing these names is to emphasize that the seemingly overwhelming chemistry of thousands of compounds can be easily understood if one understands the chemistry of a half dozen functional groups. To understand these functional groups more fully a whole course in organic chemistry is required.

HYDROCARBONS

Are compounds which contain carbon and hydrogen only. If there are no double or triple bonds then the molecule is very unreactive and can add no more hydrogen to itself; the molecule is said to be "saturated". Saturated hydrocarbons are called alkanes and have the general formula C_nH_{2n+2} where n is the number of carbon atoms in the molecule. For larger values of n, many structural isomers are possible. This is because the atoms of carbon may be linked into a "straight chain" or into a branched array resulting when three or four carbon atoms are joined to one carbon atom. The chains might then grow in three or four directions from the atom. Any of these chains might itself start to branch in several directions. One can draw many structural formulas to represent $C_{20}H_{42}$: the only restrictions are that each carbon atom must have four bonds and each hydrogen atom must be a chain terminator with one bond.

Unsaturated hydrocarbons are compounds which have double or triple bonds. They are able to react with hydrogen. The carbon-carbon double bond results from the overlap of two sp^2 carbon orbitals and the partial overlap of the partially filled p orbitals of the two carbon atoms. The overlap of the p orbitals is not efficient and it leaves loosely bound electrons in the molecule. These loosely bound electrons make the molecule more reactive than the corresponding alkane.

Example: Ethane C_2H_4 is an unreactive alkane; ethylene C_2H_4 is a reactive alkene (i.e. it has a double bond).

(a) Draw the structural formula for ethylene

(b) Predict the products formed when ethylene undergoes addition reactions with:
  (1) hydrogen
  (2) chlorine
  (3) water

Solution:
(a) Because the carbon-carbon bond is double, the carbon atoms must be using sp^2 orbitals and the bond angles are 120^0.

(b) The addition reactions are:

$$CH_2 = CH_2 \ + \ H_2 \longrightarrow CH_3CH_3 \ \text{(ethane)}$$

$$CH_2 = CH_2 \ + \ Cl_2 \longrightarrow CH_2Cl \ CH_2Cl \ \text{(1,2-dichloroethane)}$$

$$CH_2 = CH_2 \ + \ HOH \longrightarrow CH_3CH_2OH \ \text{(ethyl alcohol)}$$

In each case the half filled and only partially bonded p orbitals of the carbon atoms are attacked.

In the middle example the numbers are used to indicate that the addition has been to the first and second carbon atoms in the molecule. 2,3-dichlorobutane is $CH_3CHCl.CHCl.CH_3$: the substitution was at the second and third carbon atoms.

92

Benzene, C_6H_6, is a hydrocarbon which uses a type of bonding which is neither double nor single, The six equivalent carbon atoms use planar sp^2 orbitals: each carbon atom is joined to two carbon atoms and one hydrogen atom. The third, half-filled p-orbital of each carbon atom extends above and below the plane of the molecule. These six p-orbitals tend to overlap so that the electron contributed by any one carbon atom may move in a state of low energy any where around the ring of carbon atoms. This unusual sharing of electrons between six carbon atoms results in a stable molecule.

The formula for benzene is:

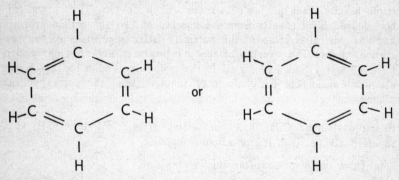

Neither formula is correct by itself, but when the pair is considered together they represent the unique bonding. For simplicity, the carbon and hydrogen atoms of the benzene ring are not usually shown. The formula for benzene by this convention is:

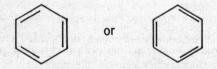

Benzene has very little tendency to undergo addition reactions similar to those of ethylene or other double bond compounds. The reactions of benzene involve the removal of a hydrogen atom and the substitution in its position of a different atom or functional group.

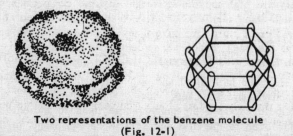

Two representations of the benzene molecule
(Fig. 12-1)

Substitution Reactions of Benzene —

(1) Benzene + bromine ⟶ bromobenzene + hydrogen bromide

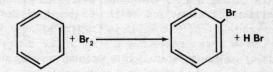

(2) Benzene + nitric acid ⟶ nitrobenzene + water

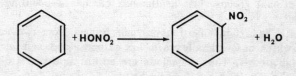

Other benzene derived compounds include aniline, an amine, and phenol, an alcohol.

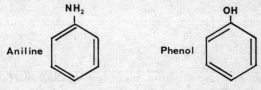

The running together of many p-orbitals in molecules containing one or more benzene rings results in close lying energy levels for the mobile electrons. These energy levels permit the absorption of some parts of the visible spectrum. The result is that many dyes and indicators are colourful because of the presence of benzene rings.

"Aromatic compounds" are compounds containing one or more benzene rings; they are sometimes, but not always, volatile and pleasant smelling.

Polymers are high molecular weight organic compounds which are formed when many identical units, monomers, are linked end to end. Just as a freight train can have many box cars with an engine and caboose at the ends, a polymer molecule has many linked monomers with chain terminators at the ends.

Polymers are formed either by "addition" or by "condensation".

Addition polymerization involves the combination of monomers with the polymer the only product. Each monomer has a double bond which is opened in the reaction. Polyethylene plastic is formed in this way from ethylene.

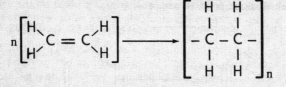

The resulting molecule is a high molecular weight alkane: the value of n is a few hundred to a few thousand.

Condensation polymerization involves the generation of a simple molecule (e.g. water) as two monomers combine. Each molecule has two functional groups, just as the box car has a coupling device at each end.

"Nylon" is a condensation polymer formed from two compounds, each of which has molecules with six carbon atoms and two identical functional groups. The compounds are adipic acid and 1,6- diaminohexane; the result is a polymeric amide.

adipic acid + 1,6- diaminohexane ⟶ "nylon" + water

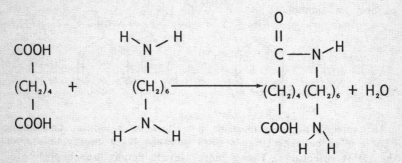

The above product still has a COOH group and NH_2 group capable of reacting with other molecules to continue the chain growth. The reaction will not occur between groups on the same molecule because these groups are at opposite ends of a fairly long chain.

Proteins are also polymeric amides formed by condensation polymerization. The essential unit is an ∝-amino acid, a substance in which one carbon atom is bonded simultaneously to both a carboxylic acid group, COOH, and an amine group, NH_2.

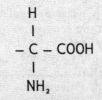

Protein chains are formed when a hydrogen atom of the NH_2 group on one molecule reacts with the OH group of a second molecule. Then the remaining OH group of the first molecule reacts with the NH_2 group of a third molecule. The "second" and "third" molecule each have a functional group remaining for chain growth. The presence of two functional groups permits the building of long molecules of almost infinite variety. These complicated, specific molecules are of utmost importance in the chemistry of living things.

EXPERIMENTS:

(a) Reactions of hydrocarbons and of alcohols.

Saturated hydrocarbons are unreactive, combustion being their only important reaction. There is no immediate colour change when pure alkanes are mixed with bromine water or aqueous permanganate ions.

Similarly, an aromatic hydrocarbon such as benzene does not react with water solutions of bromine or permanganate.

An alkene such as cyclohexene, C_6H_{10}, (the six carbon atoms are joined in a ring) causes bromine water to quickly turn from reddish to colourless; when cyclohexene is shaken with aqueous potassium permanganate, the solution changes from purple (MnO_4^-) to greenish (manganate ion MnO_4^{-2}).

Alcohols react with sodium to generate hydrogen and are oxidized by permanganate to the corresponding aldehydes and acids or to the corresponding ketone if the alcohol is of the type.

$$R - \overset{\displaystyle R}{\underset{\displaystyle H}{\overset{\displaystyle |}{\underset{\displaystyle |}{C}}}} - OH$$

(b) The preparation of some derivatives of organic acids.

Ethyl acetate, an ester, is prepared by mixing acetic acid, CH_3COOH, and ethyl alcohol, C_2H_5OH, in the presence of sulphuric acid. The sulphuric acid has a great affinity for water and thus aids the forward reaction.

$$CH_3C\overset{O}{\underset{OH}{<}} + C_2H_5OH \xrightarrow{H_2SO_4} CH_3C\overset{O}{\underset{O\text{-}C_2H_5}{<}} + H_2O$$

The amide of acetic acid, acetamide, is prepared by rearrangement of ammonium acetate, CH_3COONH_4.

$$\left[CH_3C\overset{O}{\underset{O}{<}}\right]^- + NH_4^+ \rightleftharpoons CH_3C\overset{O}{\underset{NH_2}{<}} + H_2O$$

Heating favours the forward reaction by distilling the water and the acetamide, m.p. 82-83°C, b.p. 222°C.

UNIT 13

THE THIRD ROW OF THE PERIODIC TABLE

Sodium, magnesium and aluminum (At. No. = 11, 12 and 13) are metallic solids. The strength of the bonds increases as the number of valence electrons increases. All are conductors because of the presence of mobile electrons.

Silicon (At. No. = 14) is a network solid in which each atom is bonded to four others. Almost all the valence electrons are localized in directed covalent bonds. A few unlocalized electrons cause the slight electrical conductivity. The lustre is metallic.

Phosphorus atoms (At. No. = 15) have three partially filled 3p orbitals. The result is a pyramidal molecule, P_4, in which each phosphorus atom is bonded to three others.

Sulphur atoms (At. No. = 16) have one filled 3p orbital and two partially filled 3p orbitals. The most stable bonding arrangement results in the formation of a ring molecule, S_8.

Chlorine atoms (At. No. = 17) have only one partially filled 3p orbital. The resulting molecule is diatomic, Cl_2.

Phosphorus, sulphur and chlorine are typical non-conducting, lacklustre non-metals.

THE ELEMENTS AS OXIDIZING AND REDUCING AGENTS

The metals sodium, magnesium and aluminum are readily oxidized: the $E°$ values are all greater than +1.6 volts. Substances with such strong tendencies to loose electrons must be good reducing agents.

Examples: (1) If burning magnesium is lowered into carbon dioxide, then black specks appear as the carbon is reduced.

$$2Mg + CO_2 \longrightarrow 2MgO + C$$

(2) If iron (III) oxide and aluminum are mixed and ignited, then the iron is reduced.

$$Fe_2O_3 + 2Al \longrightarrow Al_2O_3 + 2Fe$$

Silicon has less tendency to be oxidized but it does react with oxygen to form SiO_2, a very unreactive compound.

Phosphorus reacts with strong oxidizing agents such as chlorine to form phosphorus pentachloride, PCl_5, and phosphorus pentoxide, P_2O_5, respectively. Phosphorus will also react with strong reducing agents to form phosphides, in which the phosphorus has an oxidation number of –3.

$$P_4 + 6Mg \longrightarrow 2Mg_3P_2$$

Chlorine is a strong oxidizing agent: the atoms have a very great tendency to acquire electrons to complete the filling of the 3p orbitals.

$$Mg + Cl_2 \longrightarrow MgCl_2$$

Chlorine has some tendency to be oxidized. This is shown by the existence of compounds such as potassium chlorate, $KClO_3$ in which the chlorine has an oxidation number +5. $KClO_3$ decomposes when heated:

$$2\ KClO_3 \longrightarrow 2KCl + 3O_2 \uparrow$$

The final oxidation number of the chlorine is the usual –1.

THE ACIDIC AND BASIC PROPERTIES OF THE HYDROXIDES

Sodium and magnesium hydroxides are strong bases. This is because the pair of electrons between the active metal atom and the oxygen atom is shifted toward the oxygen atom. The bond is highly ionic. For example:

$$Na^+ \quad \overset{..}{\underset{..}{O}} \ H$$

Aluminum hydroxide is a white solid obtained when an aqueous solution containing hydrated Al^{+3} ions is treated with NaOH. One equation for the reaction is:

$$Al(H_2O)_6^{+3} + 3OH^- \longrightarrow Al(H_2O)_3\,(OH)_3 + 3H_2O$$

The hydrated hydroxide is amphoteric: it can act as either an acid or a base.

In the presence of a base $Al(H_2O)_3\,(OH)_3$ acts as an acid by releasing hydrogen ions to form $Al(OH)_6^{-3}$. In the presence of an acid $Al(H_2O)_3\,(OH)_3$ acts as a base by accepting hydrogen ions to form $Al(H_2O)_6^{+3}$.

Silicon forms a hydrated oxide which is weakly acidic. The bound water molecules have a slight tendency to release protons, forming the silicate ion SiO_3^{-2} which is readily hydrated.

Phosphorus has a greater affinity for electrons than does silicon. When a phosphorus atom forms a hydroxide linkage the electron pair is approximately shared between the oxygen and phosphorus atoms. When ionization occurs, hydrogen ions are released.

$$H_3PO_4 \rightleftharpoons H^+ + H_2PO_4^-$$

Sulphur and chlorine are more active non-metals than phosphorus. If atoms of sulphur or chlorine are bonded to OH groups, then the electron pair is attracted significantly away from the oxygen atom. The oxygen atom tends to become more positive and thus repel the hydrogen ion; the acids are strong.

$$H_2SO_4 \rightleftharpoons H^+ + HSO_4^-$$
$$HClO_3 \rightleftharpoons H^+ + ClO_3^-$$

As the numbers of oxygen atoms in a family of oxy-acids increase, the electron shift causes the hydroxyl oxygen atoms to become more positive and the acid to become stronger: H_2SO_4 is a stronger acid than H_2SO_3.

OCCURENCE AND PREPARATION OF THE THIRD ROW ELEMENTS

Sodium and Magnesium — occur as the ions in sea water and certain sedimentary rocks; prepared by electrolysis of the molten chlorides.

Aluminum — occurs widely as the oxide, Al_2O_3; prepared by the electrolysis of the molten oxide.

Silicon — occurs widely as quartz, SiO_2 and as silicates, SiO_3^{-2}; prepared by reduction of SiO_2 with carbon.

Phosphorus — occurs in rocks as phosphates, PO_4^{-3}; prepared by reduction with carbon and SiO_2.

Sulphur — occurs as the free element and in a variety of sulphides, S^{-2} and sulphates, SO_4^{-2}; prepared by mining the element.

Chlorine — occurs as chloride ion in sea-water and certain rocks; prepared by electrolysis of aqueous NaCl.

Argon — occurs as a monatomic gas, one per cent by volume of the atmosphere; prepared by distillation of liquid air.

TRENDS IN PROPERTIES OF SECOND AND THIRD ROW ELEMENTS

As the number of electrons in the valence shell increases to four (carbon and silicon), the molar heats of vaporization and boiling points increase.

When the number of electrons in the valence shell reaches five (nitrogen and phosphorus), the heats of vaporization and boiling points drop dramatically. The values remain low for the remaining elements in each row.

UNIT 14

THE TRANSITION ELEMENTS
OF THE FOURTH ROW

This is the set of ten elements which starts with scandium (At. No. = 21) and ends with zinc (At. No. = 30). As the atomic number increases the additional electrons are placed in the five 3d orbitals, while the 4s orbital is the only occupied level in the n = 4 state. This is because the 3d orbitals are of slightly lower energy than the 4p orbitals.

ELEMENT	SYMBOL	ATOMIC NUMBER	ELECTRON CONFIGURATION	
scandium	Sc	21		$3d^1 4s^2$
titanium	Ti	22		$3d^2 4s^2$
vanadium	V	23		$3d^3 4s^2$
chromium	Cr	24		$3d^5 4s^1$
manganese	Mn	25	$1s^2\ 2s^2\ 2p^6\ 3s^2\ 3p^6$	$3d^5 4s^2$
iron	Fe	26		$3d^6 4s^2$
cobalt	Co	27		$3d^7 4s^2$
nickel	Ni	28		$3d^8 4s^2$
copper	Cu	29		$3d^{10} 4s^1$
zinc	Zn	30		$3d^{10} 4s^2$

The only elements with irregularities in the electron configuration are chromium and copper. In each atom of these elements one of the 4s electrons moves into the fifth 3d orbital.

The elements are good conductors of heat and electricity and have a shiny, metallic lustre.

The outer shell electrons (3d and 4s) have similar ionization energies and the number of these electrons which a given atom uses in bonding varies. For example, vanadium can form the following oxides: VO, V_2O_3, VO_2 and V_2O_5.

In the interval of scandium to manganese the maximum possible oxidation number rises from +3 to +7 as the number of s and d valence electrons increases from three to seven.

In the interval of iron to zinc the oxidation numbers are generally +2 or +3.

COMPLEX IONS –

These are structures formed when a positive ion becomes surrounded by and bonded to groups which are either negative or have completely filled orbitals which can be oriented toward the positive ion. The charge of the complex ion is simply the sum of the charges on the parts.

The co-ordination number of the central atom in a complex ion is the number of near neighbours which the atom has in that complex. The co-ordination number of aluminum in AlF_6^{-3} is six; the co-ordination number of chromium in $Cr(NH_3)_6^{+3}$ or $Cr(H_2O)_6^{+3}$ is six; the co-ordination number of nickel is $Ni(CN)_4^{-2}$ is four.

Complex ions are generally highly symetrical. Six complexed groups usually become arranged to form the corners of an octahedron with the positive ion at the center. In the octahedral arrangement, any four of the complexed groups lie in a plane; the fifth and sixth are centered above and below this plane e.g. AlF_6^{-3} (Figure 13-1).

Four complexed groups may be arranged so that they form the corners of either a square or a tetrahedron, with the positive ion at the centre in either case, (Figure 13-2). $Ni(CN)_4^{-2}$ is square planar; $AlBr_4^{-}$ is tetrahedral.

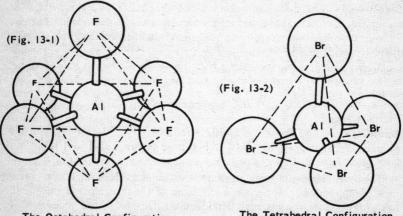

(Fig. 13-1)

(Fig. 13-2)

The Octahedral Configuration   The Tetrahedral Configuration

The type of bonding may be either ionic or covalent. The bonding in AlF_6^{-3} is highly ionic because the electron pairs are shifted toward the fluoride ions. The bonding in the ferricyanide ion, $Fe(CN)_6^{-3}$, is covalent: the electron rich cyanide ions, CN^-, supply electrons to the partially filled orbitals of the central atom.

The formation of complex ions between some cations and water results in amphoteric hydroxides. Aqueous chromium (III) hydroxide is hydrated and may be represented as $Cr(H_2O)_3(OH)_3$. This structure may act as an acid by releasing hydrogen ions from the H_2O or it may act as a base by adding hydrogen ions to the OH^- group.

$$Cr(H_2O)_3 (OH)_3 + OH^- \longrightarrow Cr(H_2O)_2 (OH)_4^- + H_2O$$

$$Cr(H_2O)_3 (OH)_3 + H^+ \longrightarrow Cr(H_2O)_4 (OH)_2^+$$

SOME PROPERTIES OF THE TRANSITION ELEMENTS OF THE FOURTH ROW

The ions are frequently coloured because the energy levels of the d orbitals are relatively close together. Electron transitions between these levels can be stimulated by the relatively low energy frequencies found in visible light.

The melting points of the elements (except zinc) are above $1000°C$ and the ionization energy is low, 150-170 kcal per mole. The values of $E°$ are positive, except for that of copper, one of the few metals found free in the earth.

As the atomic number and the nuclear charge increase across the series, the density generally increases and the radius of the doubly charged ion decreases from 0.9 to 0.7 Angstrom.

SPECIFIC PROPERTIES OF SOME ELEMENTS OF THE FOURTH ROW

Chromium – The metal is reactive but the oxide coating formed in air seals the underlying metal, protecting it from further oxidation.

Common oxidation states are +3, found in the hydroxide $Cr(OH)_3$, a green solid, and +6, found in the strong oxidizing agents chromate ion CrO_4^{-2} and dichromate ion $Cr_2O_7^{-2}$. The yellow chromate ions unite in the presence of hydrogen ions to form the orange dichromate ion:

$$2CrO_4^{-2} + 2H^+ \longrightarrow Cr_2O_7^{-2} + H_2O$$

Manganese – The most commonly encountered oxidation states are +4 and +7, as shown by MnO_2 a black or brown solid and $KMnO_4$ a dark grey or violet solid which forms pink or purple solutions in water. Both substances are used as oxidizing agents.

Iron – The metal has a high tendency to corrode in the presence of water and oxygen. The presence of hydrogen ion increases the rate. The process probably involves the reaction of the active iron with H^+ to produce iron (II) ions; oxidation by atmospheric oxygen of the Fe^{+2} ions yields hydrated iron (III) oxide, $Fe_2O_3 . nH_2O$. The value of n is variable; the product is usually called rust. Iron (III) hydroxide is a reddish-brown or rust coloured solid.

Nickel – The metal is encountered in many Canadian coins. The common oxidation number is +2, encountered in compounds such as the hydroxide $Ni(OH)_2$, a green solid.

Copper – The usual oxidation number is +2. Copper (II) hydroxide, $Cu(OH)_2$, is a pale blue or white solid; if excess ammonia is added a deep blue colour appears, caused by the complex ion $Cu(NH_3)_4^{+2}$.

Zinc – "Galvanized iron" is iron with a thin coating of zinc. If the iron starts to rust or oxidize, then the nearby zinc will reduce the iron. The zinc ions produced tend to form a protective carbonate layer. The oxidation number of zinc is +2; the hydroxide $Zn(OH)_2$ is white and amphoteric.

EXPERIMENTS:

(a) **Separation of iron, cobalt and nickel ions by an anion exchange resin.**

An anion exchange resin is composed of polymers which tend to trap negative ions and release hydroxide ions. It can be used to separate the cations of the transition series which tend to form negative complex ions such as $FeCl_6^{-3}$ and $CoCl_4^{-2}$. By Le Chatelier's Principle, these complexes tend to disappear in solutions which have a chloride concentration which is low or negligible.

When a solution of Fe^{+3}, Ni^{+2} and Co^{+2} chlorides is treated with concentrated HCl the high chloride concentration favours the formation of the negative complexes. This solution is then placed in the resin.

Any negative complex ions will be "tied up" in the resin. Washing with concentrated HCl releases green Ni^{+2} ions, indicating that this metal did not form a negative complex ion.

Washing the resin with successively more dilute HCl solutions causes the decomposition of first $CoCl_4^{-2}$ and then $FeCl_6^{-3}$. The colour of the released Co^{+2} ions is blue to pink; that of Fe^{+3} ions is yellow.

(b) **Corrosion of Iron**

When iron nails are exposed to various aqueous solutions it is found that basic conditions inhibit rusting and that the presence of hydrogen ions and other ions speeds the rusting. Ions of Fe^{+2} are detected by their reaction with the ferricyanide complex ion to produce a blue precipitate.

$$K^+ + Fe^{+2} + Fe(CN)_6^{-3} \longrightarrow KFeFe(CN)_6$$

(c) **Preparation of a complex salt and a double salt**

A complex salt contains a complex ion. $Cu(NH_3)_4SO_4 \cdot H_2O$ is prepared by adding ammonia to copper (II) sulphate solution. This produces the complex ion $Cu(NH_3)_4^{+3}$. Adding ethyl alcohol to the solution causes the deep blue complex to crystallize.

A double salt is formed when two salts crystallize simultaneously from the same solution and in definite proportions.
When bluestone, $CuSO_4$. $5H_2O$, and ammonium sulphate, $(NH_4)_2$
SO_4, are dissolved in warm water and the solution is cooled,
a new substance, $CuSO_4$. $(NH_4)_2SO_4$. $6H_2O$ crystallizes out of
solution. The colour is light blue.

(d) Preparation of Potassium Dichromate

In a basic solution chromium with an oxidation number +3 is
oxidized to the +6 state using hydrogen peroxide H_2O_2.

$$2 \ Cr(OH)_4^- + 3O_2^{-2} \longrightarrow 2 \ CrO_4^{-2} + 4OH^- + 2H_2O$$

The colour changes from green to yellow as the reaction progresses. When the solution is acidified with acetic acid the
colour changes to orange as the dichromate ion is formed.

$$2 \ CrO_4^{-2} + 2H^+ \longrightarrow Cr_2O_7^{-2} + H_2O$$

UNIT 15

ELEMENTS OF THE SIXTH ROW AND SEVENTH ROW

The Lanthanides or Rare Earths — are a transition series of elements in the Sixth Row whose atomic numbers range from 57 (Lanthanum) to 71 (Lutetium). Just as the fourth row transition series is caused by the filling of five previously by-passed 3d orbitals, the Lanthanide series is formed by the filling of seven 4f orbitals. The elements are all reactive metals which displace hydrogen from water and form tribasic hydroxides.

For reasons which are not fully understood, the oxidation number of all the lanthanides is +3 and the chemical properties are very similar.

THE SEVENTH ROW OF THE PERIODIC TABLE

The elements are all radioactive; uranium, Atomic Number (Z) = 92, is the heaviest element found naturally on earth, although there is spectroscopic evidence for the existence of californium (Z = 98) in certain stars. Elements 93 to 103 have been prepared by bombardment of heavy nuclei with projectiles such as neutrons or helium nuclei.

The "Actinides" appear to be a family of transition elements in the Seventh Row, (starting with actinium, At. No. = 89), in which seven 5f orbitals are being filled. The chemistry of the members is quite varied more reminiscent of the Sc-Zn series than of the La-Lu series. The study of the chemical properties of these elements is difficult because they can only be obtained in small quantities and because a pure sample of any one element can never be found — there will be increasing quantities of nuclear decay products.

Radioactivity is the spontaneous disintegration of atomic nuclei with a release of energy and lighter particles. It is impossible to predict when any particular nucleus will disintegrate, but it is possible to make statistical predictions about what will happen to a large group of nuclei. For example, the most durable form of the heavy alkali francium (Z = 87) has a mass number of 223 and a half-life of 21 minutes. Any particular atom of francium might survive with no nuclear change for thousands of years. If one had a sample of many francium atoms, say a micro-mole or 6×10^{17} atoms, then in 21 minutes there would be only 3×10^{17} atoms of francium left. (This type of prediction is similar to those made by life insurance companies about life expectancies). The other 3×10^{17} atoms of francium decompose to form radium, At. No. = 88, mass number 223.

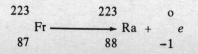

$$ {}^{223}_{87}\text{Fr} \longrightarrow {}^{223}_{88}\text{Ra} + {}^{0}_{-1}e $$

Thus someone attempting to study the chemistry of francium could be studying the chemistry of radium without realizing it. In the francium decomposition a neutron in the nucleus breaks down to form a proton (charge +1, mass 1) and an electron (charge −1, mass 0). The electron or β-particle is emitted with energy.

Radioactive or unstable elements are not found frequently on earth because their half-lives are often less than the apparent age of the earth, about 5×10^9 years; these elements are technetium, $Z = 43$ and all elements with Atomic Numbers greater than 83.

The common methods which atoms use to stabilize their nuclei involve the emission of β-particles (e.g. $^{223}_{87}$Fr) or the emission of α-particles:

$$^{238}_{92}\text{U} \longrightarrow {}^{4}_{2}\text{He} + {}^{234}_{90}\text{Th}$$

Very strong forces of unknown type, which are called nuclear forces, hold the protons together against tremendous repulsive forces in the nucleus of atoms. The magnitude of the "binding energy" which holds the nucleus together may be computed as follows: experimentally determine the molar weight of an isotope (e.g. $^{4}_{2}$He = 4.00277 gm) and then calculate the weights of the particles from which that mole of isotope was assembled (e.g. $2^{1}_{1}\text{H} + 2^{1}_{0}\text{n}$ = 4.03312 gm). The difference in mass represents the amount of matter which is transformed into energy as the nucleus is formed (e.g. 0.03035 grams is equivalent to 6×10^{11} calories of energy, by the relation $e = mc^2$).

The bringing together, or fusion, of hydrogen nuclei to form helium nuclei with a release of energy is the process by which the sun and stars release energy.

NOTES

NOTES

NOTES